Darryl's Diary

Darryl's Diary

Brian Chaucer

Darryl's Diary

Text copyright©2020 Brian Chaucer
Cover design images GoGraph.com

isbn 978-1-908577-98-6
e-book: isbn 978-1-908577-94-8

British Library Cataloguing in Publication Data.
A catalogue record for this book is available from the British Library.

1 3 5 4 2

Printed by
The Book Factory

Hawkwood Books 2020

For
The Associated Iron and Steel Workers
of Great Britain

February 4th

Welcome to the start of my new venture into the Hotel Trade, a completely different occupation to that which I have just discarded without a second thought.

Working many years as a mortuary assistant, I often yearned for some conversation and glamour in my life. I don't seem to make friends easily and find it difficult to strike up a conversation that doesn't finish prematurely when one is asked what one does for a living.

Naturally, I used to lie and say I worked on the buses or the trains - anything! - but the problem was that on the few occasions a new found friend would want to see me home I would find, on returning to the lounge after disappearing to make the tea or pour a drink, they would be looking at my bookshelves somewhat quizzically and trying to resist the temptation to touch 'The Embalmers' Trade Supply Catalogue', or read the latest article such as,

FORMALDEHYDE EXPOSURES IN EMBALMING FOR WHOM THE TOXIC BELL TOLLS

a great read incidentally, and informative, although I won't be sorry to leave this part of my past behind.

This, and my collection of interesting but minor dissecting instruments (all quite legal however) now preserved for posterity, adorn and add interest to my bookshelves but seem to make people, quite unreasonably in my view, edgy. They begin asking the most morbid questions, and as much as one tries to veer away from the subject of dealing with the deceased, it crops up again and again – often at the most frustrating of times. To get them into bed at this stage is nigh on impossible.

Even if I can get them as far as the bedroom, I find them looking at the bed linen carefully. I have long ago given up having silk on the beds as I am convinced that people thought it was made from the leftovers at work. The only odd bits I have ever brought home were a few handles that could not be used - the lacquer had started to peel – but which, with a bit of care and attention, I discovered made beautiful wardrobe handles.

Perhaps it's the job after so many years but I like dark, heavy curtains and, I must admit possibly, although I don't see why, the delightful small children's Victorian coffin I use as an ottoman at the end of the bed. However, I realise this can be off-putting for the squeamish, so if I can get to it in time I try to cover it with some old lace curtains kept just for this purpose. This, and the odours of embalming fluid which seem to linger no matter how much I quickly dash around squirting Haze air freshener, seems to add to the general nervousness and apparent recoil when gently touching or caressing, only to be greeted with, "Oh, aren't your hands cold?"

A change of life, a new career, was called for and so I have sold my house in Romford and decided to open a gay friendly guest house in S__. I did consider Blackpool, but when I looked at the sheer number of hotels, I thought there would be no way I could make a living amongst so much competition, and with so many prestigious establishments. The chandeliers and grand pianos, even curtains better than anything I have, and bed sets and drapes that I would once have been pleased to lay someone out on, plus the low prices they are charging, ruled it out.

All I can say is that some of the owners must be extremely rich and perhaps only doing it for a hobby. I don't think more than a few can be making enough to pay the electricity bills, let alone give their guests breakfasts as well. Then, of course, since Blackpool lost the casino, all I seem to have read about in the papers is the poverty and deprivation of the indigenous population and the squalor perpetrated by a lack of will on the part of local government. Strange, you people up north, friendly and warm, but you appear not to be going anywhere. It must be your fascination with pigeons.

Anyway, I found this nice, but rather run down guest house that has been closed for the past year. The owners said that now they were getting near to retirement they had lost interest and were hoping to emigrate to Spain where they had an elderly aunt needing constant care. If I was interested, they would knock £18,000 off the asking price, provided I could complete in a fortnight.

Well, you don't get offers like that every day, so I jumped into action. It seemed too good to miss, especially as it was also being sold with everything needed to get it up and running again almost immediately. Admittedly, the furnishings were old and the place could certainly do with a lick of paint, but I reckoned that with a good scrub through and a few minor repairs with my, to date, under-used tool set (I only ever seemed to use the screwdriver) I could be filling the place with all sorts of gorgeous and (with luck) available guests.

The solicitor has said that I can move in next week if I don't want to make some of the searches. I find they will try anything to bump up their bill. Water survey – why?

The taps and toilets all work! Electricity survey, the lights go on and off! Gas survey, the cooker works! It hasn't got central heating so I am definitely not wasting money on a gas survey. A structural survey - what for, just to keep a surveyor in work? The building has been standing for over a hundred years, it's not likely to fall down now. Notwithstanding all that, he then went on to suggest a damp survey. These solicitors certainly know how to bump up their charges.

All this is for the poor people who, already suffering a crippling mortgage, are then offered a home improvement loan by the Building Society. Fortunately, I can afford to pay cash, and although I may have to borrow just a few thousand for the first months whilst I build up the customers, I won't have to pay through the nose for services I don't need.

The cheeky beggar even asked if I had contacted the fire brigade. I said that I would leave that until I had a fire! The place has an alarm system with bells and buttons all over the place, and the owners said that it had worked perfectly for the past twenty years and, provided I did not turn the power off when going on holiday, it would even look after the place for me whilst I was away.

The solicitor then went on to suggest that I contact the environmental health department. What sort of mug is he taking me for? Contact them and down they will come looking at all my saucepans, telling me I need a Hoover or a washing machine, maybe even rubber gloves and a mask to cook a breakfast - although, come to think of it, I already have the last two at home.

Great! I have packed everything up and eagerly await

next Tuesday when some of my old colleagues are going to move me using a couple of the hearses. It is, after all, only a few personal bits and pieces, and they may fit in the locker under the coffin platform – that is unless my mates are off to another funeral and already have one in the space. In that case, my stuff will have to go on top, and if they a coffin on board they can drop me off before going to the crematorium.

I can't wait, and will let you know how my moving-in day goes next week. Until then I will quietly muse on the sort of guests I will take. Younger ones I think, definitely fit, and clean as well, but not too prissy. Hopefully lots of singles, so plenty of choice. But how much to charge them? Difficult one that! I don't want to put off someone I fancy from coming back, but then I do have to make a living - and with only fourteen bedrooms and a small bar, I will need to fill those rooms at least four days a week.

I will decide how much as they arrive and discover what they are into. In the meantime, I am going to suss out the local gay scene. Now, if I meet someone, I can tell them that I am a Hotelier. That should help my street cred. I may even meet another gay hotelier, although I'm not sure if I want to yet - they might think I am going to take their business. I will just have to assess the situation as it arises.

February 10th

What a day! I am absolutely fagged out! It started at five a.m. with me packing the last bits ready for the move. Fortunately, I've been able to leave all my furniture for the people I sold to, although they did insist I didn't leave the ottoman behind - the Victorian child's coffin, if you remember.

That had me praying my former colleagues, those helping me to move, could get it into the hearse along with all my other stuff. It has always proved useful, that ottoman, as somewhere to put all my porn, and a few other things I would rather no one caught sight of, so I am quite pleased to be keeping it.

They were supposed be arriving at nine but I had a phone call telling me it would be nearer ten as they were going to the crematorium first. Apparently, the mourners were happy enough to make their own way home after being dropped off at a local pub for the wake, so my colleagues were now coming straight on to me, and as they had nothing else on for the day they would be able to help me settle into the new place. They promised to bring along booze and pork pies too.

Fabulous! They arrived just before ten with just the hearse and one limo, but loads of space for all my bits. The whole crew decided to come, including the rather dishy Colin - tall, elegant and camp as a row of tents. He always looks gorgeous in his black suit, with the tight fitting trousers forcing his pride and joy to gently push on the front of them. It is usually the case that most of the mourners' eyes are on his bottom when a coffin is being lifted off or on the hearse, and he knows it! It was great when he used to help me with the embalming and I could get to put the apron around his waist, smoothing out any wrinkles.

I remember he would compare certain sizes with the deceased, and sometimes tell me he wished he could do a swap. I think those times are the only thing I shall miss about that job. Anyway, within minutes all my goods and chattels were on board - along with the flowers. They were supposed to have been taken to the local hospital first, but Charlie (constantly moaning about why of all places the crematorium is a no smoking establishment, and always desperate to find somewhere to light up, so he's always first to volunteer for burials) decided it would be a good idea to bring the flowers along to brighten up the new place.

Not being at all happy with the two wreaths, we stopped off on the way to leave them by a lamp-post, thinking that should slow the traffic down for a few days! The beer was soon out in the limo, and with the five of us discussing my new venture and all the accompanying repartee, we arrived at my new guest house in no time at all.

Thank God there was no problem parking and I was able to quickly alight and greet the sellers waiting at the front door - coats on, ready to go, luggage alongside.

They did seem somewhat shocked by having a hearse and limo arrive, but understood when I explained they were just friends helping me with the move. So inside we went for me to check everything was okay, and for us to contact our respective solicitors in order to complete the sale. Meanwhile, outside, my colleagues were starting to unpack my bits onto the front doorstep, causing occasional passers by to avert their eyes and cross themselves. Colin, thinking it would be funny, had placed my ottoman in full view of the street with all the flowers unceremoniously piled on top of it - still, it meant we had no problem with the parking warden who said we could stay as long as we needed!

Following a quick flit around the premises with the owner explaining in double quick time, and without pausing for breath, where the fuse box was, how to switch on the fire alarm should I want it and when to put out the rubbish etcetera etcetera, he showed me a lovely tired old red folder and proudly proclaimed it was the fire certificate.

It must be a good alarm to get a certificate with it, I can remember thinking, but then he went on to say it was no longer needed. Now all I had to do was write something down relating to actions should the alarm go off and state how many fire protection bits there were. He assured me a nice fireman would call to help me once it was known I had arrived. I wouldn't even have to ask. Isn't that nice of him!

I would need to pop out and get something in for my own dinner before any guests arrived, he advised me, although no guests were expected that day – it had been kept free to allow me to settle in. And at some point he suggested that if at any time a man from the council should call, so that he didn't become a nuisance, I ought only to tell him I don't do breakfasts, and then he would go away and leave me alone – and I thought that was fair enough.

The neighbours on the left were a bit funny at times

about people parking outside their place on arrival, I learned, but as they didn't own the road it was suggested I should just tell them to p*ss off. That's nice, isn't it? Apparently those on the right never spoke to anyone, and he likened the landlady there to Hyacinth Bucket - all fur coat and no knickers!

They had fallen out a good many years ago, after she had complained to the council about him painting all his outside walls in lime green, a colour which has now nearly all flaked away. It seems she only takes in refined gentlemen – exactly what I want to do, I thought, so I shall need to keep a close eye on who goes in there! Oh, and he then warned me, I will also need to keep a watch out for the people opposite.

If they see a likely guest knocking at the door, by the time I get to answer it the woman may already have legged it across the road to tell them she has vacancies and better rooms. The Bitch! It looks like I will be spending a lot of my time at the windows, and not just looking out for trade. How annoying! Anyway, the sellers had an afternoon flight to catch from Gatwick and were desperate to get away as soon as possible. Could I hope to remember all I'd been told, they wondered? And I thought, who knows? After them pushing a huge bunch of keys into my hand, of which I noted none were labelled, the sight of them almost running to get into the taxi patiently waiting across the road made me happy.

Now it was all mine!

After the waited for nod, my friends began to bundle everything into the first room off the street, 'The Connaught Bar/Lounge' according to the faded brass sign hanging on by one screw. By now there were a dozen or more pedestrians standing around outside just gawping at the scene, and I began hoping that once the coffin had been moved and there was nothing more for them to see they would quickly b****r off.

With everything inside, I decided the first thing, after my colleagues had trampled up and down the stairs, in and out of every room, and we'd suffered the occasional guffaw of laughter as one of them found a bed pan or saw the notice in the toilet about only flushing for solids, was to break open the cans and pass round the pork pies. I was hungry; I think we all were. Colin wouldn't stop though.

He continued to rush around placing flowers all about the place, whilst remembering to tear up and throw the sympathy cards into the raffia baskets which were to be found in every room. There were no vases, but thankfully he had discovered a lot of stainless steel tea and coffee pots.

By three o'clock I was hoping they would be going soon. I needed to get on with something. Fortunately, Andrew and Tom, the funny pair who love to do make-up on the deceased, and them being as straight as a die - oops! – the drivers and the only ones still remotely sober, at last said they ought to be getting back as the vehicles had to be cleaned out on their return to the yard.

So with lots of slaps on the back from them, and a quick fondle and a promise from Colin to return sometime to stay for a weekend, they finally departed. I watched from the porch as they tumbled with little co-ordination into the vehicles, all of them frantically waving and shouting ribald comments before they drove off, beeping their horns. The net curtains of the houses opposite swung to a close, and finally I was able to take a deep breath, pause, and wonder just what I had done!

After a necessary pointing of Percy at the porcelain - and at the same time regretting drinking so many cans - I managed to make myself a strong cup of tea and smoked a couple of cigarettes in an attempt to sober up a little. Still hungry, I finished off the last two pork pies and, after just one more cigarette, I began to feel reasonably okay again. I was now ready to start exploring my new home and business in earnest.

Where to start, I wondered? I know, it came to me, begin at the top and quietly and slowly work my way down, examining everything whilst soaking up the delirium of knowing it is all mine. But then in a moment of gay abandonment I decided that whilst I was there I might as well check out the Connaught Room first.

It did have a small bar in the corner, I discovered, cleverly tucked away under the stairs where the previous owner, the swine, had left four empty optics, three out-of-date bottles of lager and a mountain of old beer mats along with enough cuddly toys and cheap china ornaments to start a boot sale. Ah well, at least there were no pumps or barrels to worry about.

It was a job to see the room properly with all my belongings dumped around it and flowers placed on every available surface, but there was an old Grundig radiogram and a pile of dusty records in the corner, mostly Matt Monroe and Cilla Black, it seemed. I soon discovered the floor was a little springy in the centre, but doubtless I could put a table over that bit, and it had a not bad foam-backed carpet, although it didn't quite reach the wall or into the window bay, but by the looks of it there was some nice old lino underneath.

There was a single power point near to the door and four plugs, no, five - and two of them were four way extensions. One headed for the bar and two went to the wall lights with their wires cleverly disguised by the wallpaper pasted over them. Then there was another one which sneaked and snaked under the carpet, across the middle of the room, coming out the other side to do the radiogram and an electric fire, and yet a further one which was the supply to the television set that stood on top of a bar stool in the opposite corner.

Several old wires ran around the skirting board, disappearing at regular intervals through the walls or under the floorboards, and I can remember thinking at some point I would need to work out what they did.

I decided the first job needing to be done in there would be to get a lampshade for the centre light along with a brighter bulb to replace the forty watt, and whilst I was at it I might as well replace the old round Bakelite wall switch where the toggle dropped making the light come on whenever anyone shut the door. The window looked quite good underneath the parrot print curtains, although the paint was a little flaky, but once that is scraped away from the edges, I think the window might even open. There is one cracked pane, however the sellotape seems to be keeping back the draught, so that is probably okay. The pictures though, they do need replacing. An awful sixties picture of a black girl standing on a rock and three pictures of adorable cats - two missing their glass and one with what looks like a bit of washing line to hang it. Oh, and definitely the dart board has to go. How naff!

So upstairs it was to go now, through the door (must get a handle for the inside of it) and into the hall. It was a bit gloomy in there but again, I can get a bigger bulb and flood it with light. Once the brown and cream paint and dado rail are gone it should look quite nice.

Fortunately a lot of it was already hidden with posters and brochures from two seasons ago, otherwise it might have seemed worse. Going up the stairs I noticed they had an ever so slight tilt, and a number of the stick bits under the handrails were missing, but nothing serious.

The carpet was, as only to be expected in a busy hotel, a bit threadbare, but it might well be a patterned one. Perhaps I will give it a go with a stiff brush and some bleach to see what it comes up like.

Two floors up, and I knew I wasn't as fit as I used to be. Gasping for breath, I sat for a moment on an inviting chair found on the small landing, one made even smaller by an old wardrobe with no door and two more broken chairs standing next to the cracked sink that were all resting up there. I guessed this was where the spare furniture was normally stored.

Rested, in and out of the rooms I went, finding them all pretty much the same. There was lino up there, easy to clean. Two of the rooms had bunk beds whilst all the others had double beds, but the doors wouldn't fully open on those as they tended to hit the end of the beds. Nevertheless, once inside and the door shut there is a feeling of much more space. They all had a bedside table, and they will look good once I put a cloth over them to hide the tea and fag burns on the peeling veneer.

Something else I noticed too was the thoughtfully provided kettle with two tea bags, two sachets of sugar and two powdered milks, found in every room. The cups were rather quaint, if a bit battered and chipped.

Not your usual rubbish, they all had Lyons Corner House stamped on them. There was an electric fire that one couldn't fail to trip over in every room, and sometimes looking dangerously close to the bed. I may have to do something about that, I realised, but near the doors all the electric meters looked good. I should make a lot of money from them.

Kindly, the seller has left me with a huge pile of old two shilling pieces which the guests can buy for £1 each to put in the meters. Every room came with a sink, I checked that. Some were even complete with both taps but none with a plug. A notice above them stated,

The hot water is on from 8am to 9am and from 6pm to 8pm. Guests found urinating in the sink will be asked to leave. The Toilet and Shower are located on the first floor. Avoid using after 11pm, so as not to disturb guests sleeping. Positively no drinks allowed in the room unless purchased from the Bar. A towel is available on request for a deposit of £2.

And that covered everything adequately, I guessed.

It was then I noticed that I would soon need to tackle some of the ceilings on the top floor. It looked as if the rain had come in at some point and made the ceiling paper droop down rather alarmingly in a few places. Raffia waste paper baskets had been strategically placed, all with some water in, under the dirty brown stains on the ceilings.

It's funny I didn't notice any of that when the seller showed me around - although when I come to think of it, I recall there were no lights on up there then as he had forgotten to bring any change up with him for the meters. Oh, well, never mind. Two of the rooms had windows that didn't quite shut as well, and it was a bit like a wind tunnel, but didn't the seller say that this floor only gets used in the summer? Who wants the windows closed then anyway? There's a fire extinguisher and an easily found button-thingy to set the alarms off on the landing, so that's good.

Apparently, there are only two simple rules I need to remember about that. I should switch on the alarm system before the guests arrive and at the same time make sure the extinguishers are empty as the bastards will no doubt set them off. The only time the extinguishers should be filled is immediately before the nice fireman calls, and thoughtfully he will always telephone a few days before coming, giving me plenty of time to get rid of the bin-bags from the hall, fill all the fire extinguishers and put the fuse back in for the emergency lighting.

The sellers claimed it was pointless having that on all the time unless you are one of those posh places where they have chargeable batteries to run the lights. I suppose it makes sense. Well, although it looks like I shall have to make quite a few trips to the DIY store, nothing looks too bad. And if I can get all the doors to close properly, I'm sure it will look even better.

Going down to the first floor, I soon found the loo and shower room. It's a cubicle, and looks as if the shower has replaced the sink to use the same plumbing, which probably explains why you have to step up nearly two foot to get into it.

It smells a bit strong in there though, and the carpet in front of the pedestal does seem to be rather damp and discoloured. I noticed earlier, when taking a pee, that it tended to squelch a bit. Perhaps if I were to unscrew the window, it would help dry it out. Annoyingly, I noticed the Jeyes toilet dispenser needed refilling. I must do that soon, before it is needed. It's the type where you give it a pull and get a shiny square piece of paper out, and I haven't seen one like that for years.

On the back of the door the notice to flush for solids only and not to forget to place a coin in the meter on the wall outside before taking a shower is hard to read and needs replacing, and the shower curtain hanging on by just four of its hooks and stuck to the wall with black mouldy stuff has obviously seen better days, but a generous splash of bleach there may work wonders. I will definitely have to clean up the tray too, and paint over the rust spots.

Oh, and whilst I am tarting it up in there, I ought to get a new handle for the chain. The rust line left in the palm of your hand when you pull it is a little off-putting. I guess to wash your hands you run them under the shower. Perhaps I should get a lock for the door too.

The other rooms on the first floor are definitely a lot better, and all carpeted differently. Some are patterned, some plain, and some both. It appears the latter are made up from off-cuts of the former. Seriously worn in places, I did initially think of turning them around, but on investigation it looked like that had already been done, several times!

They are bigger rooms, with double beds, and unlike the upstairs rooms where there is just a pole across the corners with a few wire hangers on them, they all have proper wardrobes. No, they're not too bad at all. Admittedly the furniture could do with another lick of paint, perhaps white - the red makes the room too dark, especially with every door in the place being painted black - but apart from just a few missing handles (which I already have a lot left over from work) they will look fine. As with all the rooms, I will have to get up there to remove the years of dust off the corded centre lights and put in brighter bulbs, perhaps forty watts, to replace the eleven watt energy savers, but that's no big deal.

The furniture is somewhat strangely laid out in a few of the rooms, and looking at moving it about I realised that it cleverly hid the worst wear in the wallpaper, so I may very well leave them that way. Two of the rooms have their own shower and loos where a bit of re-grouting and the replacement of the missing tiles should make them look like new. These are the ones the seller said he let out as his premier family rooms as, in addition to the double bed, they also have a set of bunk beds and even come with a colour television complete with its own meter. This makes them a bit cramped but does give less carpet to see or vacuum. Another bonus on this floor is all the windows having the same pattern curtains on both sides. They don't seem to be wide enough to pull shut, but there are nets as well.

I'm a bit concerned about the inconvenience of all the wires running around everywhere in the rooms, with some of them changing from thick to thin and then back again where oodles of black insulating tape join them together. I think there needs to be more than one socket to a room so I might look into getting someone to poke a few more in. A double socket can't cost much, and it must be annoying for the guests only to be able to plug in the TV or the kettle or the shower or the electric fire one at a time and not to have them all on at once. Perhaps as a temporary measure I will get a few more extension leads in the morning. After all, I could be taking a lot more money in the meters.

With the top two floors done, it was time to explore the rest of the ground floor, so with the Connaught Bar / Lounge already covered, it was straight through to the adjoining dining room. Strangely, as I can take in 45 guests, there are only enough tables and seats for 18. I shall just have to hope they don't all come down for breakfast at once! The huge piles of plates and various other pieces of crockery in the corner, all different shapes, patterns and sizes, need sorting. I will have to throw out the cracked ones.

The tables and chairs all seem to wobble a bit, and I'm not sure if it's the furniture or the floor yet, but it would be nice to have all the same chairs in there and maybe matching cloths to cover up the worn Formica table tops. Oh dear, more expense! One of the tables has all the bottles of half-filled ketchup and brown sauce collected on it, and I was amazed at just how hard the sauce can get around the bottle-necks. I had to get a knife to prise some of them free.

A few sharp digs with a spoon into the sugar bowls soon had them loose again, so they were alright, but I wasn't so fortunate with the butter in the dishes - that had dried and turned solid. It refused to spread even after warming it up.

What a waste, I shall have to throw it! The contents of the salt and pepper pots had seemingly turned into concrete, and no amount of banging would get any to come out. Nevertheless, the two unopened boxes of cornflakes will be usable, and that's good news. They may be a little out-of-date, but I can always empty them into Tupperware containers and throw away the boxes. And perhaps with everywhere going non-smoking, I should take the ashtrays off the tables now. They could go into the bedrooms to replace the tinfoil fairy cake ones. On the whole this room doesn't look too bad at all. It won't need much more than a bit of decorating, and something done with the damp on the end wall which has made two strips of wallpaper hang free and flap around like window blinds.

When at last I arrived in the kitchen, the engine room of my empire, I noticed it smelled a bit and could see one had to be careful where one trod - the amount of grease on the floor could refill the fat fryer. The cooker too seems to be welded together with a lifetime of fat and crud, but it does work just fine. Almost as a bonus, if you put the three working rings on they give a bright orange glow, so as well as warming the place, you hardly needed to put the light on.

I suddenly realised how cold it had turned, so I left the rings on for a while. The lack of warmth everywhere began to remind me of the place I was working in until only last week. There at least the guests never complained, but here I shall have to keep it warm.

Beside the cooker, a dangling canvas-like handle emerged from a dark red tube suggesting it was the fire blanket. It looked a little rotted, and I would have tested it with a tug, but for the threatening behaviour of the multi-legged beast that had taken up residence there.

Shuddering, I turned away to study the nice modern sink with single drainer straddling a four-by-two wooden frame, and the twin tub washing machine beneath with its hose sensibly taped to the tap in the sink. That will be useful when I have to do the laundry.

However, sitting on the vacant ring, the old flat iron which would take forever to do all the ironing had already convinced me to buy a new electric one.

A huge pile of pots and pans further along under the sink were jumbled up with some old bottles of bleach and jiff, and all of them covered in cobwebs – yuk! I will have to get the vacuum in there!

On checking the contents of the fridge and cupboard I discovered the sellers had left me a bottle of sterilised milk, a box of eggs, a packet of bacon, two tins of beans, a tin of tomatoes and a packet of cocktail sausages, in case I had any guests wanting breakfast before I could get to the shops. That was kind of them. They have been so helpful and considerate, even dropping their price by £18,000 because I was able to move in almost immediately. I feel quite guilty, taking advantage of them having to sell up so quickly, and only so as to look after their ailing aunt in Spain. The poor people were in such a hurry they didn't even have time to sort out the accounts, but they have promised to post them on to me.

Suitably warmed, I ventured out the kitchen door into the yard. It is fairly big, and once all the old bricks, bits of wood and broken furniture are removed, I will be able to hang the washing out there.

The back gate into the lane beyond only needs the door frame re-screwing to the wall and a lock fitted for security. Once everything has been finished off with a lick of paint, I could even put a deck chair out there. Around a corner there is another door. Through this, steps lead down to the owner's private quarters – my quarters! It is a pity I shall have to go out into the yard to get to them, but I'm sure a bit of plastic roofing could be built over to get me out of the kitchen and through the door without being soaked when it is raining.

On route, the drain between the two doors is obviously blocked, and it stinks to high heaven, but I expect a bit of a poke with a stick will soon sort that out. And lastly in the yard there is an outside loo which seems to double up as a paraffin and cooking oil store. This will be a blessing should I need to get up in the night. I won't have to unlock the building and go all the way upstairs, perhaps only to find the loo already occupied. It has no door at the moment, but it can't be overlooked other than from the kitchen window, and nobody will be in there.

My own private quarters, in the cellar, have been nicely panelled out in hardboard and then papered, although it has warped a bit in places. A ceiling would have been nice, instead of lying in bed and looking up at the joists and floorboards of the kitchen above, but at least it has been painted in mauve (my favourite colour) and I suppose it does give me that extra bit of headroom.

The lead which comes down from a plug in the kitchen to supply the power point and light needs tacking to the wall, but that's an easy enough job, and something will have to be done about the musty smell. I shall add some air-wicks to my list for tomorrow.

The double bed has nice linen and a bedspread with a plastic sheet over it. Apparently that's in case the twin tub upstairs should leak or the hose fall out of the sink and flood the floor. A meat tray underneath it copes with any small leaks and needs to be emptied regularly, so I must make a point of doing that.

A wardrobe, a chest of drawers, both with mothballs, and some shelves along the back wall complete my room. The sellers did say they left the paraffin fire on down there all the time to stop the damp coming through too much, so if I do the same at least it will be nice and warm, and with no window down there, there's no draughts either.

So that's it folks, I am absolutely done in and will shortly be going to bed. Tomorrow is a new day, my first day as a landlady. After a quick shopping trip, I shall turn the vacancies sign around and wait for some trade. I will let you know how I get on next week. But tonight I shall dream of chicken.

February 11th

I awoke to the clattering of my alarm clock and could hardly believe morning had arrived. It was pitch black, but with a tinge of excitement it slowly dawned on me, this was my first full day at the guest house where my bedroom was in the cellar of my new empire, and it was a room without a view.

I scrambled around madly in the darkness in an attempt to plug in the light, groping everywhere for the wire. My throat felt like a sandpit and I can remember thinking that the paraffin fire is going to take some getting used to. I swore I would have the wick turned lower in future.

Bursting for a pee, I leapt out of bed and rushed up the stairs. Crikey! Those stone steps were cold, and boy did it hurt when I stubbed my toe on the razor sharp edges!

Once outside in the yard, and completely naked, I dashed towards the loo, all the time hoping none of the neighbours would spot me. With no door to the loo, I found the severe cold blasting up my rear end whilst relieving myself was somewhat kinky, although not exactly pleasurable. It promoted the decision that in future I would need to routinely first put some clothes on.

A few moments later and I was galloping back to my quarters with a paraffin can to refill the heater, still praying my journey would go unnoticed. By that time I was definitely wide-awake! Hurriedly, I dressed and made my bed, remembering to pull the plastic sheet back over the top in case, later on, I should be tempted to try out the twin tub.

Great! Arriving at the kitchen door it took a few severe

yanks before it decided to fly open. Once inside, the first task was to light all three rings on the cooker to warm the place up. Remembering I still had some of the sterilised milk left by the sellers, I put the kettle on one of the rings before trying out the cornflakes. Finding them thoroughly revolting, and unsure whether it was the cornflakes or the milk, I removed the kettle and abandoned any idea of breakfast. The orange glow from the rings, although pretty, was producing noticeable fumes which were starting to bring on a headache, so I was forced to turn them off. Never mind! After a couple of cigarettes and a good cough, I was ready to face any challenge.

I wondered if I should make out a shopping list, but in the end decided against it. I needed just about everything! Instead, I chose to try out the shower. So outside and down the stairs to my room I went again, sauntering to get my toiletries bag, and then all the way back and up to the first floor.

Damn! Cursing wildly, I trudged back down the stairs and, after hunting for a coin to put in the meter, I climbed back up again. There's so much to remember! Ramming the coin in the meter, I turned on the shower and leapt in. Brr! I tried twisting the shower knob back and forth, but to no avail. The jet stream I was expecting turned out to be not much more than a lukewarm old man's trickle, and halfway through soaping myself even that suddenly turned cold on me.

I swore again, realising the meter had run out already, and I had only brought up one coin. Idiot! Forced to finish off showering in the icy cold dribble, I quickly dried myself and picked my clothes up from off the floor to get dressed.

Blast! Unthinkingly, I had left my trousers on the damp mat in front of the loo! They did seem okay, though, so after a hurried shave, and thanking God for battery razors, it was out of the house I sprinted to do the shopping.

Sometime later, struggling back with what seemed to be the contents of the local shop packed into eight carrier bags, and frequently having to put them down to change hands, I was almost home when the neighbour came out to enquire if I was the new owner.

Hello, I thought, he is going to moan about the hearse and limo parked outside yesterday. But no, he turned out to be quite polite and amiable and asked all sorts of questions about what I intended to do with the property. Silly really, I thought it would have been obvious. I would run it for what it was, a guest house, what else? – and hopefully better than my predecessors, once I had got going with my paint brush.

But I wasn't rude in my reply, I remained polite, which may have explained why the guy offered to lend me a dressing gown to wear when running the gauntlet every morning to the loo. Oh dear, I had been spotted after all!

I learned from my neighbour that the couple before me had been trying to sell the property for years because they were keen to buy a pub in Spain. After losing their drinks licence they had even tried to sell it at auction but there had been no interest. Apparently, after losing his license, my seller had to tell people the bar was for personal use only.

The environmental health officer had paid a visit too and told them they could not continue doing breakfasts. He didn't exactly say why. But if I wanted the number, my neighbour knew of a reliable firm that could put the slates back on my roof. With the number of them that had come down into the road over the past few years, he was surprised there were any actually left up there at all.

By this time a sort of sinking feeling in my stomach was beginning to emerge. No, I thought, don't be silly, every property has its minor faults and the sellers were nice people, even making up the beds before they left and taking the details of a family that had booked in for a week next month.

Wondering about the motive behind him telling me all this bad news, I broached the parking situation with my neighbour. Surprisingly, he didn't seem at all bothered. Apparently, what had annoyed him and his wife in the past was my seller parking his pigswill lorry outside once the parking restrictions had finished for the evening - and him telling me he was semi-retired! The smell used to upset his guests. Sometimes, he revealed, instead of going to the farms to dump it, he would leave it on the back of the lorry all night, and in the summer the stench became intolerable. He went on to say that, on the whole, it was a good street, one where everyone helped each other. That was apart from the two homosexuals who had a guest house at the far end. What went on in there when they had guests, he just couldn't imagine! Oh dear! I'd better not say too much yet then, I thought. I shall have to wait and find out how the land lies.

Clearly the man hadn't got to know these guys for himself, but it was good news to know that someone else in the street was gay too and running a hotel. I decided I would need to think up an excuse to bump into them, sooner rather than later.

Back inside, I turned the vacancy sign around, just in case, and hurriedly put all the shopping away, noting that I would need to buy a new refrigerator before the summer - this one seemed to be gently warming up the contents!

At breakneck speed I tidied up the lounge, putting all the flowers in two plastic buckets I had especially bought for them, so releasing the tea and coffee pots in case they should be needed.

My ottoman I dragged to the centre of the room and camouflaged it with a candlewick tablecloth. With some coasters on it and a big ashtray it now looks like a large coffee table and does an excellent job hiding the wobbly floor. The carefully placed leopard skin patterned throws managed to hide the worst of the wear on the brown leather three piece suite, so the lounge, at last, was beginning to look civilised.

A couple of hours passed whilst I was scrubbing out the kitchen, and putting some drawing pins into the lino to hold down the rips, before the door bell rang. It was a not too salubrious gentleman clasping a carrier bag and asking for a room for two nights. It could be longer, he informed.

Bingo! My first customer!

Yes, I said, as I hurriedly invited him into the hall, I did have a room, and then suggested he went up to look at room 5, all the time scrambling to find the room key amongst the bunch left me. He returned to the lounge saying it would do fine, and telling me, if I didn't mind, that he could pay for it the next morning, after breakfast, when he had been to the bank. It was just what he was looking for, and at that time he would probably pay for the whole week. Great, I thought. Perhaps he might even stay longer than that. I had some money coming in already!

Early that evening he popped his head around the lounge door and asked if it was okay for him to come in and watch the television. Well, it is the guests' lounge after all, so I invited him in. Promptly he sat down in the very chair I had been in and, grabbing the remote control, switched the channel over to the football. So that was the end of me watching Coronation Street, and I hate football.

"Oh," he eventually asked, "is the bar open?"

"Well, to tell you the truth," I said, "I have yet to stock up for the season and just have a few bottles of beer left."

Spotting my quarter bottle of gin and litre of tonic next to the sausage rolls bought that morning for my tea, he said, "Not to worry, this will be fine."

During the rest of the football match he steadily consumed all of it, the gin and my sausage rolls! At least he has left me a sip of tonic, I thought, when later he got up and explained he was going out till quite late, but was sure that he could return without disturbing me.

"No problem, you come and go as you wish," I smiled at him, realising I had at least another £16.50 to add to his bill for the food and drink now, and that can't be bad, but also appreciating that I would need to visit the off-licence the following day for more supplies. Perhaps this time some crisps and nuts too. I did want it to look professional, after all.

Following two hours of utter boredom and suffering the man's inane chatter interspersed with roars from the football crowd on the television and his occasional bursts of flatulence, I finally had the lounge to myself again. Thank goodness!

The full ashtray, the pile of empty bottles, and the sausage roll wrappers pushed down the side of the settee cushion had destroyed any earlier illusion I may have created, but I decided to leave it until the morrow. Enjoying a few moments of peace, I made a mental note to lock the door to the lounge before retiring to bed.

I didn't want the room to become trashed further when my guest returned during the night, and I certainly didn't want him delving around under the tablecloth, perhaps in search of some drink, only to discover the secrets of my ottoman!

Before going to bed I set up a tin of beans, another of tomatoes, an egg, a rasher of bacon and a packet of cocktail sausages along with two slices of bread on the kitchen table ready for action in the morning.

A frying pan was the one thing I had forgotten to buy that day, and there wasn't one in the place. Still, no problem, I could scramble his egg, the sausages just boil, and for the slice of bacon, as it would be a waste to put the grill on for just one rasher, I could put the flat iron on a gas ring and when it was hot, press it onto the bacon.

It would probably need doing both sides, and on the draining board for safety, but I would find that out in the morning. Pleasant dreams, I wished myself, whilst thinking how grand it was to have coped so well with my first customer!

Up extra early the next morning, in the dining room I set up a clean serviette and some fresh milk in a jug next to the Tupperware container full of cornflakes. The music was gently drifting through from the radiogram in the lounge and the wallpaper on the back wall looked great now. I had used the same trick as with the kitchen lino - put some drawing pins in to hold it down.

The toilet flushing somewhere above alerted me that my guest was probably on his way down. Yes, he appeared through the door shortly afterwards, bright and friendly, clasping his carrier bag. He was going to the laundrette later, he explained, on his way back from the bank, and I remember thinking that he could certainly do with a change of clothes!

Breakfast went like a dream – well, I suppose with the exception of the cocktail sausages. They ended up looking like a load of charcoal willies. Still, what they lacked in quality was made up in quantity. I had cooked him the whole packet.

The bacon came out well. I had to be quick with the bread knife to cut it away from the bottom of the iron, and it only wanted the iron held down for the count of three, but I did have to do both sides. Anyway, my guest told me it was the best breakfast he had tasted in a long time, and he finished it as he had started, with another bowl of cornflakes.

He suggested I should provide jam. All the posh places had jam. True, I thought, and some marmalade, perhaps sealed in those little packets, and some butter too. I needed to find out where to get them from. It had made me cringe to see him coughing up over my tub of margarine whilst knocking six bells out of my table as he tried to loosen the salt and pepper.

Forty-five minutes and eight slices of toast later, he

cheerily went out the door telling me to expect him back in an hour or so to settle up for the week, and he reminded me not to forget to put the bar bill on his account. So, when he had not returned by lunchtime, I was growing rather concerned for my very first guest.

Had he had an accident? Got lost? Who would know? I kept looking out of the window to see if I might spot him, maybe in his search for the right hotel. At one point I even wondered: should I telephone the hospital?

By three in the afternoon, I thought I had better go upstairs and check his room to see if there were any contact numbers. Perhaps his mobile number was there, or that of a relative. Gingerly, I opened the door, and was immediately hit by the smell of alcohol, old socks and urine.

The waste bin was full to overflowing with empty cider bottles and cigarette butts, with ash all around it on the carpet. It was only then that it suddenly dawned on me - the bloody rotten bastard was not coming back! There was nothing but the putrid smell of him remaining in the room. Pulling back the bed covers, my heart sank and I groaned aloud. The bed was soaking wet - right through to the mattress!

It wasn't such a good day after all.

February 12th

Having put the soiled mattress in the yard, hoping it would dry out overnight, I did at last get around to trying out my twin tub. After first remembering to check the meat tray was underneath and empty, it was in with the soiled linen.

The lights dimmed a bit whilst it laboriously rumbled away at the wash, noisily and seemingly forever, but the time did finally arrive when I had to heave the sheets out of the wash part into the spinner, only to discover the sound of that had all the beauty of an express train screeching round a bend at full speed.

The laundry completed, I eventually retired to my bed. But I was unable to sleep that night. My mind kept wandering back to what the neighbour had told me about my sellers, the damp coming in through the top ceilings, and the amount of work that was required to bring the place up to a reasonable standard.

All that, coupled with the realisation that my very first guest had been one of life's wasters, ensured I had little rest. Suddenly I felt quite alone.

Hey ho! Morning arrived, it was another day, and I felt I needed a complete break away from the place, even if it was just for a couple of hours, so that I could put everything into some kind of perspective and decide what I intended to do about it all.

I had to come up with a plan of action, think about what to tackle first, and there was just so much to think about.

I walked to the pier, and deep in thought I slowly perambulated it to the end. After staring into the water for what seemed ages, and with no solutions to my problems springing to mind, I turned and immediately regretted the distance I had come. Because at this time of the year the train only runs at weekends I had no choice other than to walk all the way back.

I groaned, and felt everything was against me. On the painstaking return journey I passed various workmen in their tight jeans painting or repairing things, but overshadowed as I was with all my troubles I could not fully appreciate the visions of them stretching and bending in front of me as they manhandled their tools and materials into awkward places. My thoughts, annoyingly, would not leave the guest house, the problems, and the sinking of my ardour.

It was on leaving the pier, and still going over in my mind some of the things my neighbour had mentioned, that an idea finally came to me. I was reliving the conversation, the man's description of the street, and it was when he got to the bit about: "the two homosexuals who had a guest house at the far end" that a sudden moment of clarity washed over me.

I decided the best course of action might be to visit these two gay guys my neighbour referred to as homosexuals. They, if anyone, should be able to give me a few tips, along with some contacts for running the business - and they might also be adorable!

Reaching the far end of my road, I scanned the buildings for any telltale signs. Although I could not be certain, I felt the guest house with a huge statue of David in the window that was heavily curtained with a rose wine coloured velour, complete with ample swags and tails all cascading from a top pelmet, was likely to be the one I was looking for.

Ringing the doorbell, it was eventually answered by a portly middle-aged man with an apron around his waist. He looked every part like he had just been reluctantly prized away from some fabulous gastronomic creation. Wiping the flour from his forehead, forearms and hands with a tea-towel, he smiled broadly and calling me "luvvy" said through his teeth, almost without moving his lips, that they did not do one night stays.

He was ready to swing the leaded light front door to a close again, when I quickly explained that I had just moved into the guest house further down the road and that my name was Darryl. I hoped they did not mind it being a gay friendly establishment.

Tristan called out to Julian, exactly the same way as before.

"Yes, Tristan," came the reply. "If it's the egg man, tell him we don't want any this week."

"It's not!" Tristan retorted. "It's the new man who moved in down the road. You know, where we saw the funeral taking place the day before yesterday. Near the rest home. He's a friend of Dorothy's."

"Well invite him in then, so we can get to know him," came the reply. "Don't stand there at the door calling out like a fishwife for the whole street to hear!"

Tristan beckoned me in, and with another "luvvy" invited me to take off my shoes before guiding me into a rather beautiful lounge, as he explained they had just had the carpets cleaned. Glistening glass tables, vases of flowers (still not as many as me, I thought), fine ornaments on highly polished furniture, a chandelier of huge dimensions that one slightly ducked under to cross the room, and a carpet that enveloped one's feet in the pile greeted me. Pictures of famous film stars and naked young men adorned the white satin printed wallpaper - all signed, of course – and I wondered: had they really stayed there?

I carefully sat down on the edge of an opulent white leather sofa, opposite a wall-mounted fifty-inch plasma television screen and a futuristic stand containing a huge selection of porn, all numbered and carefully labelled, with the titles typed and laminated. Tucking myself up to the armrest to gain some purchase, so avoiding falling back into the sofa and being eaten, as it threatened to do, I looked around the rest of the room. At the end was a bar that went from one side of the room to the other.

An ornate gold coloured shutter had been pulled halfway down. Behind was a huge selection of spirits, four pumps for beers, and all of it cleverly lit with down lights and sparkling led lighting that reflected in the mirrored back wall. A huge vase containing condoms of every description and a box of poppers were neatly displayed at the end of the bar, and along the front stood a neat row of chrome bar stools with white brocade cushions. By the window at the other end of the room was a harp.

Tristan did later explain that he used to play it, but that it gave him bruises and chaffing to the insides of his thighs so now he just uses it to slice lemons for the bar. Wow! I thought. These guys know what it is all about!

Tristan left the room to prepare some drinks, and to fetch Twinkie, their little baby who just happened to be a pedigree Shih Tzu, as Julian glided in amidst his own private cloud of expensive after shave. "Hello, what's that cologne your wearing? It smells so manly," he breathed at me, and then continued on before I could answer. "So you're gay are you? And you're opening up your guest house as gay friendly.

Well, you are brave darling, but you do look so butch, so you might get away with it! We just couldn't abide straights ourselves, let alone having fish around the place as well!" he gushed. And then with a giggle added, "We could certainly do with a few more gays in Southtrend – it's strictly Naffsville at the moment!"

I sat looking up at the middle-aged man, almost agog as he appeared to hold court, and I can remember thinking: I must get the smell of embalming fluid out of my clothes. But then mused that if it smelled manly when mixed with my Brute aftershave, it might not be so bad.

The silver tray of three splendid lead crystal glasses accompanying an equally prestigious decanter of gin that Tristan reappeared with was only marred by the two-litre plastic bottle of Tesco tonic water. "Right out of Schweppes tonic at the moment - bloody brewery let us down." he quickly apologised, as a fur ball followed him into the room. And then with a camp lilt he said, "Come, Twinkie, and meet the nice new man, but don't you dare get up on the furniture."

There were no short measures, the drink flowed easily, and the three of us just seemed to settle down to a good old chinwag. They promised to take me to a good cash and carry on the trading estate, when they next went, where I could buy all the catering bits and bobs I might need at sensible prices. I thanked them for being so kind, and then let my eyes shoot around the room again, this time in search of an ashtray.

There were none, and I resisted asking for one in case they should grimace and go into fits of coughing and spluttering. So, instead of smoking, I quaffed my way through the scrumptious cheese savouries they had thoughtfully provided, occasionally allowing one to fall – accidentally, of course – to satisfy the fur ball sat at my feet staring up at me, pathetically whimpering for more than the sparse attention I had chosen allocate.

"We've been living here for six years now, dear," Tristan revealed. "We seen them all come and go, haven't we, petal?" he turned to his partner at the appropriate moment. "It was an absolute nightmare when we started up."

I smiled sympathetically at Tristan, whilst trying to avert my eyes from the undesirable fascination they had found with his khaki shorts. Loose cut, and far too minimal, from time to time as the man moved around on his chair they would reveal just a glimpse of a testicle. Now I know it's all about whatever floats your boat, but this portly, ginger moustached guy with a balding pate was doing absolutely nothing at all for me in that way.

It was an embarrassment. However convincing my eyes of that fact was an impossible task, and I began wishing it had been some young Adonis sat opposite me in those shorts. One with a huge packed lunch staring me in the face, where then there would have been much excitement in just waiting for the next slight shift in his position.

"What has made a difference for us are the nudist art weekends we introduced two years ago," Tristan revealed.

"Just using pencils, of course," piped up Julian. "We

cant be doing with all that paint and stuff in here; not with our furniture. But it was fortunate that Tristan used to give adult art lessons at a night school before we moved here to open 'The Hotel', and he had all his own equipment – easels, art paper, and all that kind of stuff."

I had already noted that whenever either of them said: 'The Hotel', and they had several times by now, it was always the loudest word in the sentence. It was conveyed with some pride and superiority, and deservedly so! I asked whether they ever displayed any of the work, or did the guests always take their sketches home with them?

"Oh, you are a wag!" Julian exclaimed. "They cant usually draw at all, luvvy! Often the only thing likely to be fondled around here is another guest's pencil!" There was a huge outburst of laughter from us all before he explained, "It works well. Our older guests all sit down naked in front of their easels, fully aware they may be called upon to pose for the rest of the group at any time, but as it happens seldom are.

Then some of the gorgeous young sweeties who just love to show off, pose for us. They get into whatever positions the group ask for, and are sometimes assisted by one of the artists. There are times when either Tristan or myself have to pull them back to their seats; some of the old queens can be a bit too frisky at times! Anyway, it is always a great evening.

The bar does well what with the older guys buying the younger posers copious amounts of drink, and they in turn buying the condoms and poppers. Next week there will even be some Viagra substitutes that Tristan has tracked down. We shall have to keep an eye on them, though - we

don't want any fatal heart attacks to find in the morning!"
Another round of laughter erupted.

"Would you like a huge box of part-used Camay
soaps?" Julian suddenly enquired, wiping the laughter
tears from his eyes. "It seems such a shame to waste
them."

"Well, yes," I said, "thank you. But why don't you use
them yourself?" "Darling, we have the best hotel in the
street. All our rooms are superior designer en-suite and
come with Broadband Internet access, direct dial
telephones, all Sky channels, a DVD player, and a top of
the range television with a twenty-one inch wall-mounted
plasma screen. Not only do we provide tea, coffee and hot
chocolate on the hospitality trays, there is a selection of
soups and biscuits too. We provide every one of our guests
with two bath towels and two hand towels daily, along
with a dressing gown and a pair of Chinese slippers to size.
When you do all that, sweetie, you just do not put used
soap in the bathrooms!"

Feeling duly told, and just a little embarrassed, I
thanked them again for the soap and said it would be
useful. Maybe I could grate some of it up for the twin-tub,
I thought, or use it for the washing up.

I was beginning to wonder how on Earth they afforded
all the grandeur, but was far too hesitant to ask, when it
was explained to me. Despite being so busy, Tristan had a
lucrative part-time job, three days a week, as a graphic
designer up in London, and although on those days it was
hell for Julian to cope on his own, it was worthwhile to
them.

After leaving his office, Tristan would spend hours

visiting as many pubs and clubs as he could handing out cards to get more clients interested in coming to S__, and especially to their establishment. Frequently it would be the early hours of the morning before he arrived home, so tired that he would simply collapse onto the bed and fall asleep before getting undressed.

What fantastic guys, I thought. And even more so when they offered to send any guests they weren't sure of to me. They knew I would be desperate for the business and that I might possibly cope with such people better than them, being as I was at the lower end of the market, and the road. Once I had my place sorted, they promised to introduce me to several other local gay guest house and hotel owners.

Apparently, many of them regularly met on Sundays in a local pub. Julian even promised to look through the cellar and the shed they had on their rear patio area for any old furniture and hotel items they no longer used, as it could well improve the quality of my premises until I could afford to buy new. It's a shame I only have a yard whereas they have a patio area, I thought as I thanked them again. They were such lovely people.

The hours seemed to fly by and too soon my new found fabulous friends were having to show me to the door, but not before making me promise to come back in a few days for another chat and to collect anything they might have found that I could have. Perhaps I might even like to attend one of their art evenings, they suggested, grinning. I wouldn't have to take my clothes off if I preferred not to on the first visit.

I smiled, briefly reminding Tristan that he appeared to

be in the middle of some cooking when I called and apologising for interrupting it. He told me not to worry, it was just a few cakes he bakes for a café on the front every morning. They love his cakes, but he could buy some at Tesco in the morning and take the wrappers off - they would never know the difference!

Once all the theatre of farewells was over, a ritual that had to include their Twinkie, I began the short walk back to my hovel feeling strangely elated. Perhaps I will have a chance to make it work, after all, I thought.

February 17th

It was Friday, a week had passed by, and in spite of that including a weekend, no one had asked for rooms. Not many people had passed by either, and that had given me lot of time to think about what others were doing with their properties in my street, and how I could enhance mine, especially considering how well Tristan and Julian had presented their place.

I might just pop along to see them again this evening if no one comes to the door here looking for rooms, I thought. Tristan and Julian did tell me I wouldn't have to take my clothes off if I didn't want to, although I would probably feel and look a bit conspicuous fully-clothed amongst all their naked art weekend guests. So, in case I did decide to go, I put my Bermuda shorts and a white tee-shirt in the twin tub, thinking that as it was only up the street, I could wear my overcoat to cover them. I could perhaps take a bottle of gin with me, as well.

Gently grating a used bar of Camay soap into the water as it swished back and forth - Tristan and Julian had kindly left me a whole box-full at the door the other day whilst I was out shopping - I watched it slowly froth up. Two bars this time, I thought to myself, and I'd remembered to put the meat tray underneath. So far, I had only forgotten it once, and fortunately then the plastic sheet had been over the bed in the cellar, so there was no damp bed.

It was ten o'clock when, at last, the doorbell rang. Racing towards the door, I wondered, a potential guest, perhaps? Quickly moving the hall rug bought earlier that week back over the threadbare section of carpet (the flipping rug has a mind of its own) I flipped the light on and gave a quick flick with the back of my hand to the rack of brochures on the wicker stand to knock the dust off, then hurried past them trying to look elegant and efficient as I reached the door.

I had to tug at it a couple of times to get it open and was thinking, I must plane the edge down a bit, the wood has got damp with all the rain. Finally being successful, I discovered a well-dressed, suited gentleman, with a briefcase in one hand and a clipboard in the other, standing on the doorstep.

"Good morning, sir. Environmental Health Officer. Just a routine visit as we note that you have recently taken over the property," he said, showing me his credentials.

How did he know that, I asked myself. It must be from when I paid the business rates during the week at the Council offices. They did ask me a lot of questions.

"I won't keep you long, but may I come in and have a look around? he asked. "Strictly confidentially, we did have a few issues with the former proprietor, so we are pleased to see the business is now in new hands. We are very approachable, you know, and most people appreciate the advice and help we can offer to avoid falling foul of the regulations," he added with a friendly smile.

I could feel I was beginning to hate the man already. Blast! I remembered leaving a cigarette burning away on the breadboard in the kitchen in my haste to answer the door. Would I be able get to it first and hide it, what with him following behind me?

"Yes, please do come in, but you will need to excuse me for just one moment whilst I dash to the kitchen. I've left the kettle boiling."

I leapt down the hall and into the kitchen. The cigarette, which by now had nearly burnt away, had left a long line of ash and a burn on the breadboard. Seizing the board, complete with cigarette end and ash, I threw it under the sink with just a second to spare before the inspector appeared behind me.

"Dear, dear, dear, this won't do at all," he muttered, whilst slickly making notes on his clipboard. "Are you trading at the moment?" he asked.

"Well, no, not yet," I lied, with some hesitancy. Then, remembering what the seller of the property had advised me to say when I moved in, and hoping perhaps the guy from the council might go if I said it, I explained, "I am not in a position to do breakfasts yet, it would be just room only until the kitchen is refurbished."

He replied by telling me in that case the sign on the wall outside should state 'Room Only' until the kitchen had been refurbished, and that I would need to advise him once the refurbishment was complete so he could inspect it. And if I was not open at the moment, then I might like to turn the vacancy sign around in the window to show 'No Vacancies'. (Oops! I got caught out there, did I not?)

Continuing, he went on to suggest that the walls should be tiled once the kitchen units were replaced, and told me not to forget that a hand-wash sink with a constant supply of hot water would be required. I needed to tile the floor too, and also ensure there was an opening window, as well as a fly screen if I was going to have the door to the yard open. The painted false ceiling tiles would have to be removed and a protected light fitting was required to replace the bulb dangling down over the cooker from its corded flex.

"You will need, of course, when I come back to inspect the progress, a cleaning schedule, a temperature record for the new fridge and or freezers," he said, clearly assuming I would be replacing them, "and some coloured chopping boards would also be nice to see. Do you usually keep your breadboard under the sink amongst the cleaning materials?" he then asked.

Oops, again! "No," I replied, "I am throwing everything under there before bagging it up for the dustman."

"You will need to enrol for a Basic Hygiene Course as I shall want to see the certificate, along with the gas safety certificate, the next time I call," he said. "And if you intend to cook for the number of guests the premises are able to accommodate, then I suggest you purchase a small commercial cooker, a heated cabinet and a bain-marie," he added, leaving me to wonder: whatever is a bain-marie?

Standing there in my kitchen, squeezing my sphincter tightly shut with the cheeks of my buttocks to stop any involuntary seepage at this devastating news, I knowledgably nodded my agreement and told him contracts had already been placed to get the work underway.

"Well done!" he said. "Perhaps I could have a look around the rooms now? But I would suggest you first turn off your washing machine. You seem to have put too much powder in it."

I watched the Camay bubbles gently overflowing the sides, as I asked, "Look around the rooms? Do you do that too?"

"Oh yes," he said. "Health and Safety covers all areas of the property for the safety of guests and visitors. Don't worry, I can clearly see that you are in the process of refurbishment, and I can give you some pointers as to what is required for when you start trading."

All this time I was thinking to myself that there was nothing wrong with the rooms, especially since I had spent the last week cleaning and pinning back loose carpets and wallpaper. However, I felt I would rather he didn't see the loo and shower room on the first floor where the carpet in front of the loo was still decidedly wet and, as I had not yet managed to free the window, it still smelled a bit off in there.

"Before we go upstairs, where is the Fire Alarm Control Box?" he asked. "I didn't notice it when I came in."

"Oh, its above the saucepan shelf, just above your head," I replied. "Move them out of the way."

It was a badly rusted old blue metal box with one switch and a green neon light, but the previous owner had assured me it had worked quite satisfactorily for the past twenty years.

"Is it switched on?" he asked?

"Not at the moment," I answered, "not until I get any guests in, but I just have to knock this switch down beside it." At which, with pride I put the switch down, and much to my glee the little green light came on. Great! It works, I thought.

"Obviously you must have plans, along with your refurbishment, to replace this with an L2 system that meets current guidelines. Who are you using to do the work?" he enquired.

"Oh, I have yet to decide that," I said, wondering what he was on about, and why he kept on talking about refurbishment? The alarm was working okay, and the light glowed nicely on the panel. Admittedly I had never actually tried to set it off, but that was only because I didn't know how to.

He went on to say it clearly had no battery back-up, and probably hadn't for years. It was useless, and should have been changed years ago. He couldn't understand why the owner had not been prosecuted for it in the past. Tutting to himself, and gently shaking his head, he asked if I had done a Fire Risk Self Assessment yet? Wondering what he was on about, he was seriously doing my head in, I told him that I was waiting for the new system to go in before I did this - whatever 'this' actually meant, so he instructed me not to take any guests in prior to all that being completed. In fact, he even advised me not to have friends staying anywhere above the ground floor until then. Cheeky Bugger, I thought!

"As with all these properties in this street, you must ensure the fire exit door to the adjoining premises is free and able to open, either with the key attached in a 'Break Glass' box or by a handle set behind glass that can be broken to gain access to open it in the event of an evacuation being necessary. You will certainly have one on the top floor landing," he said, "and maybe on the first floor as well. Especially at the moment whilst you are here on your own with a totally inadequate alarm system, it is essential the door is in full working order."

By this time I was desperate for an evacuation myself, but I didn't dare leave him on his own. God only knew what he might find next! Door, what door? I thought to myself. There was definitely nothing on the first floor, and the second floor landing just had an old wardrobe, a couple of broken chairs and a cracked sink on it. Surely there was not a door through to 'all fur coat and no knickers' in the adjoining guest house? I couldn't believe that someone should be able to just come waltzing into my property unannounced whenever they had a fancy to. As soon as this guy from the council had gone, l would definitely go upstairs to check behind the wardrobe on the top landing.

"Well, I will quickly have a look around the rest of the premises, the inspector said, making his way to the dining room. Then, drawing a breath, he stated, "That house brick shouldn't be propping the door open. I've already noted the doors need new closers. If you keep the black springs on the middle of them you will soon have the neighbours complaining about the constant slamming when you have guests. And don't forget intumescent strips are required on all the doors to the bedrooms, if they are not already fitted. As most of these older places still have the original panel doors to the bedrooms, you might find they will need replacing with approved regulation fire doors."

"Of course, it is something I have in hand to do before I open," I blurted out, whilst feverishly rushing back into the kitchen to soak up all the bubbles with a tea towel, and at the same time puzzling over the 'into-something' strips. Into what? Had he momentarily drifted off into some foreign language? It almost sounded perverted.

The mopping-up job quickly done, I rushed hotfoot behind the man into the Connaught Bar-come-Lounge.

"Interesting coffee table. Well, all of it, I suppose - the

parrot print curtains and the furniture too," he remarked. "God, how did the former owners live in such squalor? You certainly have your work cut out here!"

It was as much as I could do to contain myself, but contain myself I did.

"I assume," he said, peering down at all the extension plugs in the wall socket, "that you have either got the electricity installation certificate or you have included a rewire in your plans. You will need to have a PAT test certificate for all the appliances too, including those in the guest rooms."

I was thinking, what now? Not more to do? And who is this Pat, or come to that the Marie he mentioned in the kitchen? People he knows in drag? He may be saying everything in a nice friendly way, but the man is a nightmare!

"You have a bar in the corner I see, Darryl," he said. "That must go if this room is used as a residents' lounge. That is unless you intend to obtain a licence for it. If so, I would suggest you instruct your solicitor to make the necessary representations to the council. They will then advise you what floor plans are required and the procedure for the submission. Knowing these properties, I suspect there will be no space for easy chairs in all the bedrooms, so do you have provision for a Dry Lounge?"

He's noticed the damp wall in the dining room, I thought. "Not quite at the moment," I replied, with my mind petulantly turning to, 'If he thinks I am putting armchairs in the bedrooms and running the breakfasts upstairs, he is seriously mistaken!'

Checking his watch, he wrinkled his brow and said,

"Time is getting on and I am quite a bit behind now. It looks as if you know what needs to be done and are getting on with it, so there is no point in me looking around upstairs at this time. I guess it will be in pretty much the same condition as down here so I will come back in a few weeks to carry out another inspection. That's if I haven't heard from you earlier to say you are ready to trade."

He gave me his business card along with another form to fill out at some time and return to the council offices before shaking my hand and wishing me luck in my new venture. Remarking on what a brave man I was, he then added insult to injury by telling me the fire extinguisher by the door was empty and seriously rusted around the bottom. I needed to replace the extinguishers and should not forget about the fire blanket that had seen better days in the kitchen. Then after wiping his feet on the carpet inside the front door, he stepped outside and with a cheery wave departed.

That's twice I've been called 'a brave man' recently, I thought. My legs were trembling, my mind whizzing around with all that I had just heard. How could this be right? In the last half-an-hour I had been told I live in a tip, and with a smile, too! It was almost unbelievable that there were so many rules and regulations to be obeyed when running a guest house.

The seller had told me it was easy - like having friends round. You just take their money, give them breakfast and change the sheets on the beds once a week, or sometimes you might get away with merely smoothing them down. Money for old rope, he called it.

I was desperate for the loo and used the time sitting in

there to calm down and think about all that needed doing. I still had around £3,000 in the bank, and I guessed a lot could be done with that, perhaps all of it. A few phone calls to find out were needed pretty urgently.

There might even be enough money left over to have the outside painted, and perhaps the windows fixed, too. At least if I bite the bullet now, I realised, I won't have to worry anymore. Yes, I decided, that was what I would do. Tomorrow I shall have a day on the telephone, but tonight I will visit Tristan and Julian. They might even be able to help me, and anyway their nudist art weekend will at least take my mind off the problems for a while.

February 18th

After the horrendous visit from the Environmental Health Officer, I was looking forward to an evening of fun with Julian and Tristan amidst their guests. Coronation Street had finished some time earlier so I guessed that the Nudist Art Weekend would already have started. Wearing my Bermuda shorts and a nice white tee-shirt under my overcoat, the smell of formaldehyde being all but completely gone, and taking with me a bottle of gin and some crisps in a carrier bag, I braved the rain for the short walk to their hotel at the end of the road.

On reaching their place I noticed the curtains were tightly shut with not a chink of light anywhere coming through. Ringing the bell summoned Julian to the door.

"Oh, hello Darryl. Take your shoes off and come on in," he said, before leading me through to the lounge as he explained that they had not received any bookings for this weekend's Nudist Art Classes. They had just the one couple of guys in at the moment, regulars who had already gone out to the gay clubs for the evening. They usually came several times a year, just for the one night, and had never been interested in mixing with the other guests or joining in the fun.

As we entered the lounge, Tristan was leaning forward from the settee, fumbling with a remote control in a frenzied attempt to stop a porn movie they had been watching. Having paused it, fast forwarded it, turned the volume up and then down again, he threw the remote onto the floor and then went over to switch off the video player at the wall socket.

"Look who's come to visit us, it's Darryl," Julian said gleefully.

Turning his head round before getting up from his knees, Tristan asked, "Have you got anything on under that coat, Darryl?" He began stroking my calf with his hand whilst trying to peer beneath my coat, then got up to assist me in taking it off, fumbling with my buttons, all the time castigating Julian for not offering to take my coat off earlier. His hands seemed to be everywhere!

I apologised that I had arrived prepared for the Art Classes, explaining that rather than embarrass anyone by being formally dressed I had chosen to put on my Bermuda shorts and a tee-shirt for the evening. Perhaps I ought to keep the coat on, I suggested, or go home again and get changed.

"Oh, what a tease you are, Darryl! We wouldn't think of allowing those lovely hairy legs to be hidden under a coat," Julian stated, going on to assure me that it made no difference at all. They might themselves change into something lighter for the evening. The two guests that had gone out just before I arrived usually stayed out until the early hours, he explained.

Tristan relieved me of the carrier bag containing the gin and crisps.

"I think it will be a fun evening, after all. But it wasn't necessary for you to bring anything. You could have bought anything you wanted at the bar. Anyway, we'll forgive you this time, you minx," he said, walking over to the bar and replacing an almost empty bottle on the optic with the bottle from my carrier bag. "We'll use this one first as we don't usually sell the cheaper brands," he said, adding with a smile, "and as you have brought the gin we won't charge you for the tonic either."

With the enthusiastic help of his partner, he eventually managed to divest me of my overcoat, which Julian whisked away out of the room to be hung up in the hall. Much to my somewhat nervous embarrassment he returned within seconds and, looking me up and down whilst licking his lips, commented on my 'fabulous body'.

Tristan piped up from behind the bar, where he was pouring the drinks.

"Just look at how well Darryl fills those shorts! He'll need both hands for sure to get them off," he said, before casually dimming the lights.

We all laughed.

"Where's Twinkie?" I asked, missing their dog and trying to change the subject as I sat down on the edge of the settee, crossing my legs and keeping a steady grip on the arm-rest.

"Oh," explained Tristan, coming over with the drinks and a selection of small cakes, "he has got used to being locked in our bedroom on Friday and Saturday nights. He became such a distraction to the guests, especially on the Nudist Art Weekends when he would constantly run between them all, sniffing and licking their private parts as they sat at their easels. I swear some of them encouraged him, and it gave him such bad breath. I will just pop upstairs and check he is all right whilst I put something more comfortable on."

"That's a good idea, I think I will do the same. We won't be a moment, Darryl," Julian said. "You just make yourself comfortable for a while, and do help yourself to anything." And with that he hurriedly followed his partner upstairs.

Sitting there alone, I seriously wished I had telephoned them before coming. I would have learned there was to be no Nudist Art Group that night, and could at least have worn something more sensible. I was beginning to worry that Tristan and Julian might have something on their minds other than just a social chat for the evening and, as nice as they were, I was not comfortable with them being quite so forward or familiar.

The prospect of spending my time dodging and evading their advances all evening had got me into thinking of an excuse to leave early without offending them. I didn't want to hurt their feelings, after all they had been helpful to me, but I wondered what I could do or say to at least slow down their advances. Tell them my crabs were clearing up nicely or my haemorrhoids were not so bad tonight? No, that was a bit too extreme.

I would simply have to hope an opportunity to escape early would arise, and perhaps sooner rather than later.

Julian and Tristan both appeared at the doorway with a 'TA-DA!' in unison. They had dressed in white togas, cut far too short, I thought to myself, and with lots of giggles and lifting of hems to reveal they had nothing on underneath, they twirled up to the seats where they plonked themselves down. Tristan sat right next to me and Julian on the chair opposite with his legs apart.

Putting his hand on my knee, Tristan asked, "Would you like to be my slave, Darryl?" He slid his hand along my thigh and groped my crotch.

"I prefer, just for tonight, you didn't do that. A nasty

rash has come up under my Bermuda shorts and it is irritating me like mad," I told him. "Perhaps I grated too much soap into the twin-tub," I added, thinking it was not a bad excuse, and one that should slow their advances. But I was wrong.

Julian immediately retorted, "Oh, you poor darling! You must let me put some cream on it for you. I know how much a rash can irritate, especially in that region. When I had a dose of venereal warts last year, it was terrible." He smiled sympathetically. "Bur fortunately it's all cleared up now," he quickly pointed out.

I replied in some haste, telling them I was allergic to medication and that, as long as I didn't move around too much, it wasn't too bad. I expressed how sorry I was to spoil the evening and suggested we could perhaps do it again another time. They both sighed, almost in unison again. Tristan told me not to worry, they understood and could sympathise, and then suggested I might like to watch a porn movie instead. Julian, who had quietly been fondling his private parts underneath his toga, nodded with a broad suggestive smile. Raising his eyebrows, he removed his hand from underneath his toga and grabbing one of the cakes from off the table, he offered it to me.

"Perhaps not tonight, on both counts," I said. "The excitement of a porn movie might irritate my rash, and as I have already eaten, I don't fancy a cake at this time."

Tristan got up quickly, clearly a bit miffed, and said it was about time he refreshed the drinks. Enquiring as to how I was getting on in my guest house, he collected the glasses and walked over to the bar.

"Yes," Julian asked, "have you had any guests yet?"

I then went on to relate the story of my one and only guest that had disappeared without paying, and also told them of the visit earlier in the day from the environmental health officer.

Returning with the fresh drinks, Tristan pushed a lemon through the harp standing in the window bay before plopping a thick slice of lemon into each glass and, much to my relief, sitting down at the other end of the settee.

"Well," he said, "when you have been in business as long as us, and no offence Darryl, we can see that through your limited background and standard education you may not be able to grasp the technicalities of a commercial venture, but we will help you as much as we can. Obviously you will never be able to reach our standard, but you could fill a niche in being able to serve the less affluent guests with their lower expectations, and that without too much effort."

Julian chipped in with, "Yes, I sometimes wish we didn't have to bother with all the scrubbing and cleaning. I don't think they appreciate it. They leave our rooms in a terrible mess at times, condoms and empty beer cans everywhere, the bloody plebs!"

"You see Darryl," Tristan continued, whilst giving an almost reprimanding glance to Julian, "it does take a certain amount of flair and style, an appreciation of the arts and the finer things in life, to be able to attract the right kind of guests by providing them with a more exclusive ambience for their stay. Unfortunately, this quality is almost inbred in one, and it is not something that any normal person could aspire to readily, not without years of training, no matter however hard they try. We are well known and respected amongst the elite business community of the town. Perhaps we might even introduce you to some of them in the future, when you have tidied your place up a bit."

"That's a good idea," said Julian. "Maybe we could take him to our hoteliers' supper next month. We don't have to say where he is from yet, and I'm sure we could lend him some decent clothes to wear. No offence darling," he turned to me as he revealed, "but you do look a bit minging at times. We've remarked on it before, when we have seen you walking to the shops, haven't we Tristan?"

Suddenly the conversation had taken a turn that I was not entirely happy with, but I brushed those thoughts aside as they continued to give me the benefit of their wisdom in where to obtain some financial help and how to sort out my place. They did give me lots of ideas, it has to be acknowledged.

Julian suddenly said excitedly, "We have been having a good old sort out, and you might like to have all the stuff we have put in a pile in the corner of the patio," whereupon they both jumped up and beckoned me to follow them out into the yard - apologies - the patio!

They had found quite a few items that might be useful to me, including an old Bain-Marie that looked as if it would clean up well, a gas cooker and lots of curtains and bedding, the latter all matching. There was a fridge-freezer they said they no longer used, too.

"You are welcome to it all, Darryl. We are sure it will be useful to you, and it does save us having to find someone to get rid of it. Let us call it £200 for the lot. How soon will you be able to take it away? We can't possibly leave it on the patio for long, we wouldn't want our guests to see it."

Gob-smacked isn't a strictly accurate description of my thoughts, but what else could I do other than agree to buy it? Yes, it would help me no end, I was sure of that, and I could make several journeys to collect it tomorrow. Perhaps my neighbour might lend me his sack barrow? I reticently affirmed that I would take it.

That sorted, we all returned to the lounge to finish our drinks. The time was getting close to midnight by now, so I thanked them both for an entertaining evening, explaining that I ought to get back home as I did have a busy day ahead. I wanted to not only pick up the stuff from their patio but also to contact the financial planner they had told me of earlier to enquire about a loan or mortgage so that I might get the environmental health guy off my back. I suggested too that Twinkie may be crossing his legs by now and bursting for a pee.

Julian retorted, "Oh, don't worry about Twinkie. He will be perfectly happy. We have a litter tray in our bedroom so we can leave him as long as we like. He's such a darling!" Then with a smile, he added, "You can pay us anytime you like for the stuff, there's no hurry as Tristan doesn't go the Bank until Monday."

At that, we all got up and said our farewells, with both of them fumbling to get my overcoat on, Julian gently fondling my crotch and saying how he hoped my rash would clear up soon, whilst Tristan gently cradled my bum in both hands and remarked on the firmness of my buttocks. A farewell kiss and I was out of the door.

Walking home, relieved it had stopped raining, I began to feel a little unsure about these guys.

February 19th

After everything that had happened, this was the first chance I had to check out the gay scene locally. Throwing caution to the wind, in view of my new financial situation, I decided I was going to have a good time. I might even get lucky and meet someone to talk to. It would at the very least be a chance to eye up the talent.

A short walk away was a club that intrigued me. It was called 'Blobby's'. A strange name, I thought, until I arrived inside and it became apparent it was a club for those with a few extra pounds around their waist, and their admirers. This was indeed a novel twist and one which seemed to work as it was fairly busy. A line of guys were sitting at the bar, presumably on bar stools, although only the legs of the stools could be observed emanating from the well-proportioned bottoms spread out on them.

Managing to squeeze between two of these people to get a drink, I found they were a friendly crowd. It appeared I was more than welcome, with several advances and offers of drinks coming my way. Unfortunately, there didn't seem to be the same proportion of smokers in this bar compared to normal gay bars, and the smell of aftershave and wind hung heavy in the air. Everyone appeared to be perspiring profusely.

Could it be me, I thought? However, it was not my scene, and so it was down the hatch with the drink and then off to discover what the 'Capricious Man' bar was like.

This was not far from Blobby's, down a back alley behind the shops on the main road. The entrance was a small door that had an even smaller flickering neon sign above it. Having paid the doorman / bouncer / cashier a £5 entrance fee, I made my way up the dimly lit stairs. On opening the heavily padded pair of green vinyl-covered doors, I was immediately assailed by the horrendous volume of the sound system.

I made my way through the haze to the bar. There was no fear of slipping as, with all the drink and chewing gum on the carpet made visible only by the cobwebbed covered spotlights hung from the jet black ceiling, one's shoes felt as if they had Velcro attached to their soles. The place was busy, and it was almost impossible to see the small stage at one end through the mass of bodies watching the second-rate drag act, one which was followed later by the almost obligatory stripper sporting a grotesque-looking tool. The more lascivious older clientele, drooling with open mouths, were at the front of the crowd and the stripper was allowing the lucky few to feel his member.

I managed to get a drink from the all-lesbian bar staff. This was a picture in itself, as the well-proportioned buxom wenches leaned across the bar to hear what was being ordered. Often there was a beer pump perfectly positioned between their bosoms and they would envelop the pump, apart from the black and brass top.

Exploring all the corners of this quite large bar, one with a dining area that sold chicken in a basket with chips and nothing else, it appeared to be built over at least six of the shops fronting the main road. Even so there was not much chance of me meeting someone here, I thought to myself. Everyone appeared to be part of a couple or group, and anyway the volume would certainly put a stop to any attempt at conversation. I decided on another drink and a visit to the loo.

Cautiously making my way across the wet slippery floor to the urinal, I discovered there to be more urine on the floor than in it. Fabulous place, were you to be into water sports and kinky for the smell, I thought. The cubicles were no better, with locks that did not lock and huge peepholes big enough to poke all manner of things through. Of course, there was no paper, and all the pans were nicely decorated inside with the remnants of the former user's curry.

Standing there at the urinal quietly doing my business, watching the cigarette butts floating past and briefly helping them on their way with my jet stream, I was joined by a guy who, glancing sideways at me, said, "Hello, have you just moved into our road? My partner and I have seen you about. Weren't you coming out of Julian and Tristan's place last week wearing an overcoat with no trousers?"

The upshot was that this guy and his partner owned a hotel not a dozen doors away from me. They, as did most of their friends in the trade, kept themselves to themselves in order to fit in with the community without antagonising or threatening them, a system that worked well.

After a few more questions he suggested I should go with him and his partner to another bar where we could hear ourselves talk. As a bonus, I was told, we would not have our elbows sticking to the tables and the ashtrays would not be hidden under piles of dog-ends.

Thank goodness, I thought. Standing there whilst hanging loose was not the most inspiring of ways to have a conversation, especially as so many of the other users seemed to be cross-eyed. So it was a zip-up and a splash across the floor again as, picking up Patrick's partner Dave en-route (I had learnt their names by now) we made our way out and headed for the Freedom Tavern.

My new friends revealed the club we had just left was a great place if you wanted a rent boy or needed to buy some drugs, and the stripper there was usually quite good, but only if you could stand the host, albeit apparently a nice man, bellowing out his repartee of old show songs and gags that rarely changed.

Barely ten minutes walk and we were at the Freedom Tavern, a traditional looking pub where, with no entrance charge, the doorman merely waved us inside. Great, I had already wasted a fiver at the previous place. The main bar area was nicely decorated, and furnished throughout with sofas and small tables. It had discreet and unfussy lighting with no music, just the hubbub of everyone talking, yet there was hardly a seat empty.

It seemed to be popular with a mixed gay crowd. Apparently the place was always full as it never had any music or entertainment. People went there just to enjoy each other's company whilst being able to have a conversation. What a great place, I thought. I will definitely come back here again, especially if I get lucky.

Someone at the back of the room was frantically waving over to us, and Patrick and Dave acknowledged them.

"Come on, Andrew and Kelly from the Pastel Hotel have got seats for us with the rest of the gang," said Patrick.

Dodging the elegant glass collectors who were skilfully performing their duties, and emptying the ashtrays, we made our way through the sea of leather seating, all occupied by people laughing and talking animatedly to each other around the coffee tables. My friends introduced me to everyone as the latest newcomer to the area, and I was fired with all the questions like how was I doing, what did I intend to do, and who did I know already? We were soon joined by another couple, and then by even more people. There was a vibrant gay community here with all these hoteliers and guest house owners, some of them having places much smaller than mine, too.

Having related my experiences so far, they went on to tell me they were working on an idea of setting up a small group amongst themselves. They wanted to share advertising costs and to help each other by having an internet site where they could communicate and share information. Nothing formal, they were at pains to point out. They would not have a chairman or a committee, or even members as such, as they wanted to ensure they could invite only those whom they actually wanted. They would pick up the costs of running it by each in turn paying any costs or bills as they occurred out of their own pockets. Perhaps, when I had finished my refurbishment, I might like to join them, they went on to suggest.

"Are Julian and Tristan going to be part of this?" I asked.

"No," came the reply. They were deemed to sail too close to the wind with their naked art groups and it was felt that they might bring the group into disrepute. Seemingly, they were not well liked by those present. Later on David revealed that Julian and Tristan had told a friend of his they had found a mug to part with £200 to take all their rubbish away for them, thus saving them having to pay for the council to remove it. Huge roars of laughter ensued, until I admitted that it was me that had bought it. Then there was an embarrassed silence, but only momentarily, it was quickly followed by more roars of laughter when I showed them that I was happy to join in with their enjoyment.

Changing the subject, someone began enthusing over a website they'd recently seen which listed all the gay hotels for Blackpool and ran informative articles about the local gay scene, suggesting they should attempt something similar.

"Don't be silly," said John from the Adventure Holiday Flats, "something like that would cost a lot of money to set up, and you would probably need a degree in computing and literature to make it a success. Even if we found someone to do it for us, they would want at least three or four hundred pounds a year. They might be able to afford that in Blackpool, what with all their chandeliers and grand pianos, but we certainly can't."

I was excited to be amongst this group, all running businesses and still sharing their free time together. Plans were made to include me in the group and to invite me to their coffee evenings. They said they would also help me by passing on decent bookings that they couldn't accommodate themselves. Wow! What a stroke of luck it was meeting this crowd. I feel now that I truly have some friends in the area. The night just flew by and by the end of it, although I had not met anyone I fancied or who was single, I had a smashing time and got quite frazzled.

There had been the one guy though that caught my eye

whilst I was at the bar getting a round of drinks. He was probably about twenty-five years old, and cute. Sidling up to me, he started talking and seemed impressed when I told him I had a guest house. He had for a long time been looking for someone just like me to share his life with, and together set up a home. My interest picked up. He was remarkably cute, wearing one of those black net-type vests, tight, with his nipples cheekily poking through the mesh. The white silk trousers, that I swear would show even a pimple through, had a slight stain at the front, but never mind, accidents happen.

Whilst we spoke his hand was on the small of my back, and he was gently moving it up and down from my shoulder blades to the top of my buttocks where gently his wriggling fingers threatened to explore further. I asked him what he did for a living and he told me he was on disability at the moment, 'under a psychiatrist', because he had a phobia about going into both open spaces and crowds, so he could not work. Funny, I thought, what's he doing in here then? He was having trouble with his landlord over the amount of rent he owed, plus the landlord was getting rather heavy about his missing television and video recorder. The lad had only sold them to Money Converters to try and reduce the arrears.

"What more does the landlord want"? he pleaded, before then claiming the council had mucked up his housing benefit. He was gradually coming off drugs, his methadone was being reduced and he was due to attend an Alcoholics Anonymous meeting in a few days time, but for now he was just going to get 'well and truly pissed' for one last time. All he needed was for someone to give him a chance, he explained, telling me then how gorgeous and what a hunk of a man I was and how he bet I was great in bed, too. Throughout all this time his hand had continued rubbing my back, and was now roving further and further afield as with his other hand he grasped mine and pulled it towards his groin.

He did ask if my place had a bar, and tried to convince me not to give it up, suggesting that if he lived there he could run it for me as he never went to bed before six or seven o'clock. That's when all the best films on the television ended. He even said that he could do all my cleaning and shopping in the afternoons, when he got up. He was a devoted type of guy and completely monogamous for the special man in his life. And apparently that was me!

For some reason, although I felt sorry for him and even lusted after his cute body, my interest was beginning to flag a tad. Preferring not to pursue this conversation any further, and by now having been served my round of drinks, I told him I had to get back to my friends.

At this point he began to shed a tear, and I wondered, was it the cigarette dangling from his mouth or the sheer lust for me? He begged me to give him a chance and to let him go home with me, just for the night to see what a wonderful time he could give me. Whatever turned me on, he could do it!

After giving him the money for another drink, I bade him farewell and returned to the group. I felt cruel, and not a little disappointed with myself, that I had not given him my address when he'd asked for it. Such a cute, good looking boy, would I regret missing this opportunity of someone so loving and caring who was willing to share my life with me?

When I arrived back at the group, one of them said he'd noticed I'd met Shaun at the bar. He was concerned in case I had given him my address, or worse, arranged to meet him. I soon learned that everyone but everyone had been there, and some coming away with more than they went with. If he fancied someone, sometimes he didn't even charge them. Oh, yes, he was a regular for some of Julian and Tristan's guests.

Phew! That was a close one, I thought.

March 5th

A fortnight passed by and with my new found wealth, the mortgage money in my bank account, work on the refurbishment of my property stormed along at a great pace. The three roofers were the first to arrive, and within a couple of days a scaffold was erected. By day three they were busy stripping off the roof.

On day two the carpenter turned up, and by the end of the day had managed to pull off every door in the place and stack them in a huge pile right up against my outside loo. The builder and his two mates arrived that afternoon to start putting in the en-suites and immediately started to knock down some of the dividing walls between the rooms.

Day three saw the arrival of the electrician and his four cute helpers to rewire the place, and put in a new fire alarm system. They immediately got to work by pulling up all the floorboards. The two guys who were going to render the outside of the building quickly followed them. They set up camp in the yard. The sacks of render, a cement mixer, an old tin bath for pouring the mix into, along with a humongous pile of doors and builders rubble, soon made it impossible for me to get to my bedroom in the cellar.

On day four the double glazers arrived, and by the end of the day I had no windows in the place at all. They insisted that as the place was obviously empty it would be okay to rip out all the windows at once and get rid of them. Where did they end up? In the yard, of course. I was left praying it wouldn't rain.

In a blind panic, on day five, I searched through the local paper and found an advert for rubbish removers. I contacted them and they duly arrived to give me a price to shift everything in the yard, along with all the old furniture still in the rooms. Just as well as all the workmen seemed to be using the wardrobes and beds as saw-horses.

The rubbish removers thought Christmas had arrived early for them and quoted me £250 a day for however long it took to shift it all. I had no alternative but to agree as by now it was impossible to move in the yard or get downstairs or use the loo, and the various workmen coming in and out to get materials were beginning to argue amongst themselves and threatening me with walking off if I didn't get it sorted.

Thank goodness the rubbish removers soon started on shifting it into their clapped out old Transit Luton van. What a relief! But as fast as they removed it, by the time they arrived back the yard was full again with my old furniture, lino and carpets, with the workmen constantly adding to the pile each day.

By now there were eighteen people hammering away, banging, with each team seeming to have a portable radio tuned to a different channel, and all of them on at full volume. Most of the men swore profusely at getting in each other's way, and there would be the occasional crash as another piece of internal wall was knocked down, only to be followed by a huge pall of dust that hung in the air. The only loo still working was on the stairs, and I found myself forced into joining the line of men waiting to use it, so it was absolute heaven to see them all depart in the evenings.

Unable to use my bedroom, and with no electricity as the electrician had cut off everything, leaving just a long extension lead to the first floor so the workmen could continue to use their power tools, I was having to go upstairs to use the builder's kettle, and was living on the eggs I could boil in it. Fortunately, it held enough water for me to also make a cup of tea using the builder's teabags and mug, and to get a shave with what was left. With no lights, no television, no heating and the only place left with a few floorboards still down being behind the front door, it was there that I had to bed down in a sleeping bag.

I spent the evenings gingerly stepping over the joists as I perused the rooms, surveying the progressing work. Of course, my new found friends I met in the club had all invited me to spend the nights with them but, with no washing facilities or being able to get to my clean clothes in the cellar, I was beginning to smell just a tad ripe, so I declined their offers. My personal hygiene was confined to boiling the kettle and pouring it into an empty paint tin in order to wash my important bits with a Jay cloth. Once I had tipped the dirty water out of the window, I made sure I always replaced the cloth over the builder's mug, as I think it was with that he cleaned it. Fortunately, I was awoken each morning by the post dropping on to my head as the postman shoved it through the letter box. It allowed me just enough time to make a mug of tea, shave, and use the loo before they all started to arrive again.

By the second week it was starting to take shape. The outside looked fabulous, the windows were in, the roof was on and the rendering was coming to an end. Inside, the electrician had put the power back on and I had light and electricity. The central heating guys arrived and were delighted to find all the floorboards still up, so within hours they were trundling in with bundles of copper pipes and radiators, spreading them around the rooms in preparation. Soon afterwards they were drilling holes everywhere. The builders had been marvellous. The en-suites started to take shape, the loos and showers were all in place, and new sinks fitted in all the rooms. With new fire doors throughout, ones that actually shut, and quietly, the place was already taking on the air of a half-decent guest house.

I seemed to spend all that week going back and forth to the shops for the zillion bits and bobs wanted by various tradesmen, along with the then daily visits to the bank to withdraw even more money. When I thought of how much money I was getting through, I could feel the beads of sweat on my forehead.

With the builders assuring me that all the floorboard would be down again, and that his painters had already started to redecorate the rooms, the carpet fitter was organised for the end of the week. The rubbish removers were reduced to calling just twice a week, and at last I could get down to my bedroom. That is until the builder started on it. He told me it needed to be tanked out, whatever that is, and he will put in a loo with a saniflo. Apparently that makes the poo run uphill. Yuk! Still at least it will mean I won't have to use the outside loo anymore, so I plan to have that removed, especially after the incident last week when the manhole in front of the yard lifted and logs began to float away, out under the yard gate and into the drain in the alley. Panic stricken at the awful smell, I had the plumber investigate. It seems it had been partially blocked for years. The last straw for it - or should I say dump? - was the workmen all using the only loo still working.

Thank goodness it was soon sorted. After a lot of prodding and poking, stirring and jet hoses, I spent the next couple of hours cleaning the yard and sweeping the alley free from all the logs that were quietly amassing by the kerb, before any of the neighbours noticed.

The carpenter started on rebuilding my kitchen, fitting all new units, and I bought a new automatic washing machine to replace the twin tub. Next week all the new beds and furniture are due to arrive so I am keeping my fingers crossed that within another week or so I can start to trade.

As luck would have it, a leaflet pushed through the door last week, one of those that had landed on my head whilst sleeping on the floor in the hall, was from a guy who built websites. Just what I needed, I thought, although I had yet to buy a computer. When I telephoned the man, he told me that having one was unnecessary as he did it all himself. He could build a site for me so anyone in the whole world could see the details of my place. All I had to do was to give him the information and tell him what I wanted to say. He would even take some pictures in colour to put on the site, including a picture of me, and all for a cost of just £500 plus vat. For this he would also maintain the site for me. If at any time I wanted to change some details, all I had to do was simply telephone him and he would do it instantly for just £30 plus vat.

I asked him how anyone would find me on the world-wide web thingy, and he explained that if anyone put my web address in their browser (whatever that is) he would guarantee my site would come up as number one on the first page of the search engines. Naturally, I have agreed that he goes ahead. He's such a nice man, too. He said he would get onto it straight away, and would not stop until it was done and on-line. I do hope he doesn't have to stay awake working on it all night.

With everything coming along nicely, I can at last hope for the hordes to start arriving soon.

March 28th

Another frenetic week passed. My builder guy seemed to have taken over completely the organisation of all the trades people and appeared to spend all his time chasing them and ensuring they had done a good job and not sloped off to the pub or taken too many tea-breaks. Consequently, he had most of them finished and out by Tuesday. He even checked their invoices, questioning some of them and getting reductions before bringing them to me for payment. What a star this man is! I am quite happy to allow him free reign.

I have decided that whatever his final bill will be, I will slip him a couple of hundred pounds on top as I shudder to think that with all that has gone on, how I could have managed it by myself. The place is looking grand, and now only the painters are left.

The builder, Gary, is about fifty years old, rugged, and definitely butch. He says he is married with four children who have mostly grown up and moved away, but he likes working in gay places as generally they are friendlier and less trouble when it comes to paying. Apart from one or two, where he had to fend off the clients who wanted more than a rub down and a lick of paint, he has always been quite comfortable with the gay community and more than happy to engage in some of the camp repartee. I did at one stage wonder if he might be bi-sexual, and given that he was as ugly as sin, I was on my guard, but it was unnecessary, he just seems to be a genuine guy and a friendship has built up between us.

After a few hurried phone calls on Tuesday afternoon,

I managed to get the carpet fitters to come on Wednesday, and the furniture delivery to be delayed until Friday. Gary suggested I should take a break for a few days as he could organise the carpet fitters, and even see the furniture was put into the rooms on delivery. What a fabulous idea, I thought. If I forgot about the holiday abroad that I originally intended, I could have a long weekend away. I felt more than comfortable leaving Gary to look after everything.

Now as it happened, Patrick and Dave, whom I had met a few weeks ago, had been calling round to see how well I was progressing with the work, and they'd mentioned that they were going away that weekend to Blackpool for the Pride march. I decided to give them a telephone call to see if it was possible for me to go along with them. They said yes, and were over the moon telling me they could easily squeeze me into their hired mini-bus. Apparently there were eight of them going.

They had all managed to book their accommodation, but in several different places, and felt sure that at this time of the year I would have no difficulty in finding somewhere to stay. Patrick printed me off a list of hotels from the internet and I spent most of that morning frantically telephoning hotels and guest houses in the North Shore of Blackpool. They all told me they had been booked full for months, but eventually I did find one which had a last minute cancellation. Ideally, it was one street away from where all the others were staying.

Friday morning arrived, overcast and pouring down with rain, but nevertheless I was excited to be going away with my crowd of new-found friends. Before too long, the mini-bus pulled up outside, and with glee I was soon inside and seated. There was over three hundred miles of seemingly constant traffic jams and lousy weather to contend with, but still the journey just seemed to fly by with us all talking about what we were going to do, and with some of them swapping their horrendous guests' stories, I did learn a lot.

Patrick and Dave had been to Blackpool before so they knew all the pubs and clubs, and so an itinerary was planned in great detail as we were driving along. We intended to do as much as possible for the weekend and had until our departure on the Monday morning to make the most of it.

The excitement grew as we approached Blackpool on the last bit of the motorway, and as the famous Tower came into view there was a frantic scramble for the maps. Patrick and Dave, having travelled by train on previous occasions, suggested we needed get to Blackpool North Station as from there the accommodation was just around the corner - every corner, apparently - and they knew their way around from the car-park behind the station.

Before we knew it, we were parked up with our luggage in our hands, off to our digs. Mine was the first we came to, and with a wave the rest of them promised to come back and collect me in an hour, once they'd settled into their own accommodations close-by.

Gingerly, I knocked on the door, carefully replacing the knocker before the owner answered it and discovered it in my hand. Seconds later he opened the door and I was immediately aware that he had only one leg. Apologising for the hopping noises behind me as I made my way to the reception window, he explained that he was about to put his false leg on when I'd knocked. He suggested that perhaps I should find my own way up to my room once I'd paid, and pleased to find he was making no extra charge for the Pride weekend, I gladly agreed.

With keys in hand, I went off in search of Room 11 which was on the top floor. Climbing the stairs, I passed the shower and loo on the first floor which, I can remember thinking, was reminiscent of my own place, but without the smell and the damp patches. Onwards and upwards to my floor I went until I found my room.

It was not one with an en-suite, of course. I had booked much too late for that, but it was a nice room all the same, and it came with a sea-view. I noted there were only four other rooms on this floor, and I could hear conversations from behind two of the other doors on the landing, so I was not on my own. The place appeared to be filling up already.

I was pleased to discover that everything worked in the room, including the television and the huge panel heater on the wall. At least I wouldn't have to wait on the landlord to decide when the central heating went on, I thought. There wasn't any! Perhaps I should have had individual heaters installed in my own place, I contemplated, then only the occupied rooms would be running up my heating bill. However, it was too late for that now.

I decided I would make myself a nice cup of tea, once I had worked how to fill the large electric kettle that just wouldn't fit under the tap. Changing my mind, I began to unpack, and soon got used to automatically ducking to avoid the sloping ceiling to the dormer window as I moved around.

Everything looked bright and clean however, and the bed was comfortable, and that being so made it hard to believe how the accommodation was so cheap in Blackpool compared to anywhere else in the country.

Admiring my sea-view, I caught sight of my friends coming up the road and dashed downstairs to meet them. En route, I bumped into two guys coming out of a bedroom on the first floor. A quick exchange of hellos ensued and I discovered they were also there for the Pride. I left them quietly arguing about what they should wear for the night as I continued down. Passing the landlord, who was busy booking in another couple, I noted he had fitted his false leg and now appeared to be quite sprightly. Seeing him with a set of teeth and a toupee, I thought to myself that he looked surprisingly attractive.

We decided to walk to the nearest gay bar for a drink before exploring the sea front. On the way, we had to pass the hotel where Patrick and Dave were staying. The owners, two gay girls, were out the front polishing the windows. They spotted Patrick and Dave and he introduced us to them. The girls seemed genuinely pleased to see us and invited us inside for a drink at their bar. They had a nice place, spotlessly clean and bright, and an hour went by enjoying their company before we left, all agreeing to return later.

Just next door was where two others in our party were staying, and it was suggested that perhaps we should have a drink there also as they were eager to show off their accommodation. It turned out to be just as swish as the last hotel, and just as friendly. The two guys running it were busy leaping about all over the place with bags of laundry and crates of beer whilst attempting to talk to the guests.

Looking out through the window I could see the whole street bedecked with bunting, and almost every establishment had huge gay flags flying. I watched as numerous taxis and minibuses appeared, constantly dropping people off outside various hotels along the street. Wow! I thought. Perhaps I'd bought a hotel in the wrong town. This place was busy!

Having one more drink at the bar gave us a chance to see the owners of two other nearby hotels. Apparently, they had popped in to discuss some last-minute Pride arrangements and already they appeared fagged out. They were talking constantly on mobile phones that looked as if they were glued to their ears, and all the time they were rustling papers and barking orders.

Just as quickly as they had appeared, they left, making a dash for the door to avert some crisis on the pier. Blackpool was amazing me, everyone was busy but still friendly. I'd met some of the people actually involved in organising Pride and apparently they were owners of their own hotels. How did they manage to do it all?

It was a great evening. We managed to get into at least four bars and a club that were all packed out. We didn't care, and by two in the morning, following one last nightcap at the two gay girls' hotel where Patrick and Dave were staying, we were all ready for our beds and looking forward to Saturday morning when we'd agreed to meet up and go to the pier to see the parade.

Up bright and early, we duly met and traipsed down to

the pier, braving the wind and the occasional shower of rain. It was interesting to see all the activity of police and organisers, busy doing whatever it was they had to do, and the excited expectation of the crowds waiting for the parade to come along, wondering what would happen next.

Andrew, one of our party, managed to put his foot through the railing we were leaning against, only to discover he was unable to extricate himself. After several unsuccessful attempts to release him by various people, which included one of them using a jar of something called elbow grease, he was finally freed by the fire brigade who, after alarmingly shouting, "It'll have to come off!", to the relief of a pastey-looking Andrew, cut off the railing with an angle grinder.

We all felt duty bound to go with Andrew to the local hospital for his swelling ankle to be checked out and treated. Fortunately, the casualty department was not busy when we arrived, and after only an hour or so we were back at the pier, just in time to have missed the parade. Disappointed, we bought our wristbands and went off to check out an obviously popular bar called the Merrie England by the pier entrance.

Finding it packed, long before the cabaret was due to start, we decided to give it a miss and made our way along the pier. Windy wasn't the word for it, and we stood momentarily enthralled, looking back at the whipped up high tide crashing mercilessly against the sea-wall. The market stalls that we were told would be lining our route had been moved because of the high winds, and we discovered them later, safely under cover at the end of the pier.

We spent several hours there milling around with the crowds, looking at the stalls, sampling the music of the dance arena, popping in and out of the afternoon show in the theatre, and just generally soaking up the atmosphere. Occasionally we would stop to marvel at the detail, colour and extravagance of some of the costumes people were wearing, and of course we were helping to keep the bars in business too. They were just as crowded this end of the pier, of course, but nevertheless the bar staff were doing a remarkably good job maintaining the throughput, with no-one having to wait too long before being served.

It was after I don't remember how many that we discovered not all of our party had seen the Pleasure Beach. It was one of those places on our itinerary, and as the time was getting on we decided we needed to visit it then if we were to get back to the pier for the evening entertainment. Everyone agreed it was a mega place with so many different rides and so much activity, but we weren't keen on the groups of what we took to be football supporters, or the obvious stag and hen groups that at least came across as intimidating and crude, considering the number of family groups there, too.

After an hour of looking, but not going on any of the rides - it was just too windy and cold for us to brave them, and Andrew was limping and having difficulty keeping up with us - we decided to go for a meal.

Back in North Shore, in the town, we came upon a sort of steak restaurant on the first floor of a building almost opposite the main post office. The meal was remarkably good and we all enjoyed it, but we did feel a bit like characters in a Dickens' book as we sat by the window watching all the beggars outside the Post Office accosting pedestrians as they passed by. There seemed to be an inordinate number of impoverished people around. Those that weren't begging were to be seen staggering along the road with cans of beer or bottles of drink in their hands, a scene frequently interrupted by passing stag and hen parties, all vying with each other seemingly trying to outdo one another in making the loudest noise or the most obscene gesture.

So far the day had been fantastic, and following our excellent meal we decided to return to our respective hotels for a quick freshen up and a change of clothes before meeting up again outside the pier in time to catch the Pride Concert in the theatre. Well, I don't have to tell you what a fabulous evening it turned out to be at the theatre. You will have all read about it somewhere or seen it on the news by now. But when racing up the pier to the show, we did bump into one guy who I must mention.

He seemed quietly elegant, with an air of friendly superiority, and he stopped long enough to take a group photograph of us, telling us it would appear on the Pride website. How exciting, we all thought. Then, saying he was due in the green room to meet some gorgeous people, as quick as a hare he was off legging it along the pier. At this point, I began to wonder what went on in the green room. I had heard of the darkroom, the backroom, even the sadomasochist room, but never the green room. What could they be into in a green room? I continued to wonder.

After the theatre we each decided to go our own way and to meet up the next morning, Sunday, at the largest of the local bars as apparently the Pride was to continue on in the venues that day. Making my way back to my guest house, going along the street where the others in our group were staying, I could see it was alive with gay couples and groups coming and going in and out of the various hotels. Looking through the windows as I passed by, it was plain to see all the bars in the hotels were busy, and the hubbub of chatter and laughter, along with the music, was wafting out into the street. I was grateful to be staying in the next street up, and in a guest house without a bar, as I was tired and would appreciate a quiet night's sleep.

Sunday turned out to be just as exciting and awesome as Saturday, as we spent the whole day going from venue to venue to see various acts. We finally ended up in a club, the Flamingo, to finish off the night. A stunning place, all chrome and steel and on several levels; it impressed us.

At about two in the morning, I think, anyway it was about the time we were beginning to flag, all the fire alarms went off and we were shepherded out into the street. In S__ they just shout time, but it does take them longer that way to get rid of everyone and close up. It was an abrupt end to the evening, but still a fabulous one. There would have been no way any of us could realistically have gone on for much longer anyway, not with the prospect of the long drive home in the morning.

Monday morning arrived and for the first time I made it down for breakfast. My landlord, smart and attentive, was clumping backward and forwards to the kitchen with the guests' breakfasts. That too became an enjoyable experience, especially when I realised that not everyone in the house was gay, but all were encouraged to - and did -

take part in conversations, with no-one being in the slightest bit bothered about who was who or what.

It was a great weekend away from all the work going on at home, but once we were back on the mini-bus for the return journey, I found I was looking forward to seeing just how much had been done in my absence.

April 3rd

We were making good progress on the way home from Blackpool, all a bit shell-shocked after the Pride and each of us nodding off from time to time. So once we had made it past Birmingham on the motorway we decided it was time for a comfort rest at one of the services, and a change of driver for the last part of the journey.

At the till, we emptied our wallets of what seemed to be enough money to pay all the staff a week's wages in return for a miserly lukewarm excuse for a cooked breakfast. It has always amazed me how with all the island self-service pods in these cafeterias, along with a huge long hot self-service counter designed to serve maximum numbers of people in record time with the least contact with any staff, one still just stands at the end of the queue to shuffle a tray along at a snails pace, continually stopping and starting to watch the odd hand appear from the line of people in front to grab a cake, sandwich or a cooked breakfast.

The only member of staff that is to be seen, apart from the occasional one sauntering in through a door behind the counter to throw some more chips or sausages into the hot dishes and have a prod and shuffle amongst what is already there in some vain hope of stopping it all coagulating together, is Dolly at the cash register. She is there to eye the contents of the trays as they reach her, and every now and then consults her price board whilst tapping away at her machine for what seems an eternity.

Occasionally she will casually get up to fill a teapot or to dispense a coffee before returning to her cash register, but the real bummer comes when you get to be the next one to pay and you find she first has to change the till roll. After ferreting around under the counter for what seems ages, she will slowly unwrap the new roll before attempting several times to feed it through the machine, and all the time she will be doing this without even a smile or the slightest eye contact. It must take nerves of steel and special training.

This ritual over, eventually we found ourselves an empty table and, with many a humorous exchange, sat around it to pick at our breakfasts. Sitting nearby, with just a mug of coffee on his table, was a lad of about twenty-five. He was surrounded by two giant holdalls and a huge rucksack, and appeared to be enjoying our banter. Quietly smiling to himself, he would occasionally glance in our direction.

Shortly before we were about to go ourselves, he got up to leave, and struggling to grapple with all his belongings, gave us a friendly wave and a nod goodbye. We watched him as he slowly made his way out of the cafeteria, and whilst I was musing to myself what a good-looking lad he was, Andrew piped up, "Wouldn't chuck him out of bed!" His partner, Peter, responded with, "You're a right old queen - you'd have anything in trousers!" There was a general consensus of agreement about the lad amongst our group, and some general discourse followed on the lad's finer visual attributes and his obvious fitness.

Back in the mini-bus, refreshed and setting off again, we were about to enter the slip road onto the motorway when we noticed the lovely lad again. He was standing by the side of the roadway thumbing for a lift. As one, we all shouted, "Stop!" Peter, who had taken on the driving, pulled over, and the lad peered in through the front passenger window.

"Where you going?" Peter asked. "We're going as far as S__. Any good to you?"

"Oh, thanks guys, that would be great! I was making my way to London, but I've always wanted to go to S__. Would it be alright if I went all the way with you?"

"You can go all the way with me anytime, sweetheart!" Peter laughed.

A broad smile crossed the lad's face. Clearly, he was not at all phased by all the laughter erupting inside and, after throwing his baggage into the back of the mini-bus, he clambered to sit beside me, shuffling around to get comfortable in the only seat available.

"Alright there now are you, Darryl?" Peter joked. "Don't think I can't see what you are getting up to back there!"

An embarrassing flush crept across my face, and I hoped no one had noticed it. Turning, I saw the lad's broad grin again, only this time it was directed at me, and suddenly I began to feel very hot. I could feel his warm thigh up against mine and he had his arm pushed gently into my side. His voice was soft and gentle, and the slightest movement from him gave me a distinct tingle in all sorts of places, soon necessitating me to casually place across my lap the copy of the Birmingham Mail I had bought earlier at the services.

The name he had provided us with, Lance, conjured up all kinds of exciting thoughts in my mind, and occasionally I would get just a whiff of his ginger hair which was almost in ringlets, though not designed to be so. He had a slight, almost sweet, natural aroma that made me want to give him a hug, but I resisted and just continued to enjoy his closeness.

Lance explained that he had left home in Burnley. His family had never understood him and were always deriding him for not having a proper girlfriend. In the rubber factory, where he worked, he was constantly chastised about his hair, and for his fondness of his Steiff teddy bear collection, which now amounted to a dozen.

He hoped to be re-united with them soon, once he had finally settled down somewhere in his own place. Before the rubber factory there had been several jobs. He had been a plumber's mate, a carpenter's mate, and for a while had even worked in a bus garage helping to service the fleet at nights. His best job, he revealed, was being a hotel porter where he had done everything from helping the domestic staff to kitchen portering.

However he hadn't been able to cope with the permanent split shifts, or the dreadful wages. Anyway, all those jobs had allowed him to accrue enough savings to see him through a couple of months in digs whilst he looked for some work and a new life down south, he explained.

This was all music to my ears. He actually wanted to work, had been working, and even had money saved up to get him going. I was beginning to suspect too that he might be gay. What could I say to him? I was working on it when Patrick interrupted my thoughts.

"Hey, Darryl," he said, "surely you can put him up for a while. With all his job experiences, he may even be able to give you a hand with some of the work."

He then went on to explain to Lance what I had been up to, and how we were all hoteliers returning from the Pride weekend in Blackpool.

I was quite overcome with the idea of having some help, and the company of this lad, so I smiled questioningly at him. He avidly agreed, and told us how thankful he was that it had been his absolute good fortune to have met us. Now all I could think about for the rest of the journey was that I was actually going to take this beautiful boy home with me - Lance - and I kept saying the name in my head. On my lap, further re-arrangements of the Birmingham Mail frequently took place.

Naturally, and quite coolly, not wanting to give away my enthusiasm, I explained to Lance that it would be only a temporary arrangement and that he would have to stay on the top floor of my place. It was not an en-suite room, I hastily added, and he would need to do all his own cooking, cleaning and washing. He was definitely not allowed to bring friends back, and I expected him to go out every day to look for work.

I would go with him to the job centre initially to get him registered, and with luck he would soon find work and be able to get a home of his own. At the back of my mind had emerged my meeting with Shaun in the Freedom Tavern a couple of weeks ago, and what a lucky escape I had then, so I was trying not to go overboard.

"Take no notice, Lance," Peter piped up, "he will soon have you in his bed. He is too shy to say so!"

More deep blushes emanated from me as they all had a good belly-laugh amidst many ribald remarks. Glancing at Lance, I could see he was blushing too, and that pleased me immensely. Peter could be so embarrassing at times, and I told him so, but secretly I was appreciative of his and the groups' comments, and their encouragement. Could it actually be true that I was coming home from Blackpool with a souvenir of my very own? It seemed so unbelievable.

We finally hit S__ around five and I was dropped off with Lance outside my guest house. Wow! It looked fantastic! Lance seemed equally impressed as he struggled with his belongings and followed me up to the front door.

Dave, the builder, had seen the mini-bus pull up and opened the front door before I could get my key in the lock.

"Hello Daryl, did you have a good time?" he enquired, glancing behind me at Lance. "Is this going to be your first guest? Its not all quite finished yet, you know."

He looked Lance up and down again, and then gave me an approving wink.

God! More embarrassment!

"No," I quickly told him, "it's just an old friend who has come to give me a hand opening for business. He'll be staying for a while, of course. I'm putting him in one of the rooms at the top."

"Of course, Darryl. Just joking," Dave said, with yet another sly wink. Turning towards Lance, in a friendly but authoritative manner he told him, "You make sure you look after Darryl or you'll have me to answer to."

Hastily, I gave Lance a room key and told him to make himself at home whilst I caught up with the progress of the house with Dave. The place looked magnificent, all carpeted, and Dave had put the delivered furniture into the rooms. There was just so much to look at, and clearly I was going to be busy in the coming week putting up new curtains, making beds and shopping for breakfast stock for the guests.

My bedroom in the cellar had been finished and now it seemed to be perfectly dry. There was a radiator on the wall and even a little cupboard with a loo and a shower inside it. Hooray! I thought. With the new washing machine upstairs it was the end of the plastic sheet on the bed, and the radiator meant it was goodbye to the paraffin heater too.

Dave explained that next week he would demolish the outside loo and then build me a porch from the kitchen door, right around the corner, and along to the entrance to my new bedroom. Before going home an hour later, he showed me how to work the central heating system and the fire alarm. Great!

After he'd gone, I had the place to myself again. Well, almost, and with some excitement I began to wonder how Lance was doing.

After quickly checking the lovely new units in the kitchen, all empty, no food, not even a tea bag, off I went upstairs. I found Lance lying on his bed reading my Birmingham Mail with the door open. If only he knew what that had been covering all afternoon, I thought to myself! I had to pinch myself at this vision prostrate before me on the bed - fully clothed, I might add, but there in my own house.

"Oh, hello Darryl. I thought I would wait until you had finished with your builder," he said apologetically, slowly sitting up to put his shoes on again.

In my best matter of fact manner, I suggested that we should go out for something to eat. My treat, just this once, I told him. Afterwards we would have to go together to the all night Tesco and he could give me a hand to do a big shop. He was more than happy with the idea and immediately up and ready to go. To see him, so gorgeous and responsive, made me go weak at the knees. My mind questioned, did he ever stop smiling? And I hoped not.

It was only a fish and chip supper that we had in the town centre, but it was enjoyable. The visit to Tesco afterwards had resulted in three trolley loads of shopping and a taxi ride to get it back home. Finally we had it all packed away and then the lad surprised me by offering to pay for some of it.

"Don't be silly, you can work it off," I told him, immediately castigating myself for not putting it better. "Would you like something to drink before going up to bed?" I asked. "We have gin and tonic in stock now. Would a short nightcap be in order?"

"I don't drink alcohol," he explained. "I can't stand the smell, but I don't mind others drinking it. If it's alright with you, a cup of tea would nice."

Tea and a packet of garibaldi consumed saw both of us yawning repeatedly. I suggested it was time I retired to my bed. "If you get lonely up there or want a drink during the night just come down and help yourself," I told him. "I have my room downstairs, out through the kitchen door."

Damn! Had I truly said that? I wondered what he would think of me. Oh, my God! I guessed he would probably lock himself in his room all night. What an absolute tart I was!

"No problem, Darryl. Thank you for taking me in, I have been lucky in meeting you. I am so grateful. See you in the morning. Goodnight and God Bless," he bade me before disappearing off upstairs.

I could not keep awake any longer, went down to my bed and was soon fast asleep.

I was awoken by footsteps above, in the kitchen. It was three in the morning, my clock told me. The noises were a bit muffled through the new ceiling, and I listened carefully, wondering whether I was being robbed, then realised it was probably Lance remembering how I'd told him he could make a drink in the night if he was thirsty.

Ardently listening, I began to imagine him up there making himself a cup of tea and felt almost comforted by his every movement. Then I heard the kitchen door being opened. With bated breath I waited as I heard him coming down the stairs, slowly and quietly.

In the gloom I could make out that he was wearing red silk pyjamas under a white dressing gown, and was carrying two cups of tea. There was a copy of *Woman's Own* tucked under his arm, as he gently sat down on the edge of my bed and in almost hushed tones asked if I was awake.

"Yes," I croaked, at a loss of anything else to say to this vision. "I thought you might like a cup of tea if you were awake," he said quietly. "I'll leave it here for you and go back up to the kitchen. I thought I would have a read. With all the excitement of today, I couldn't sleep. Luckily, I thought to grab one of my mum's magazines before I left home, to while away the time hitchhiking."

"No, no, no. Stay and have a chat with me if you are not

tired. Sit back on the bed and I will prop some pillows up for you," I spluttered as I patted the pillows up and smoothed out the duvet for him to, hopefully, lie back on.

He climbed onto the bed and made himself comfortable. We talked for what seemed to be hours, until both of us actually fell asleep, him first and soon afterwards myself. I can remember glancing at him in the duskiness and looking at his soft complexion. He was still smiling.

The last thing I remember doing was putting a spare blanket over him, he being on the top of the duvet and me underneath. I was seriously tempted to give him a gentle goodnight kiss on the forehead, just a little one, but fearing he might wake, I resisted the urge.

What absolute bliss it was. Then I thought to myself, what a strange choice of magazine Lance had made! Perhaps it was the only one he could find at the time.

April 4th

I was awoken by Lance bringing me a cup of tea in bed. Dressed, he apologised for disturbing me during the night and went on to say that he was going to start on putting up the curtains in the rooms and would then make up the beds before going to the Job Centre.

The morning was going remarkably well until answering a ring at the doorbell. On opening the door I discovered a family standing on the doorstep, along with a mountain of luggage and four children. There was a youth of about fifteen with his sister who was perhaps a year younger. Both of them looked like seventies punk rockers with attitudes to match.

A further sister, a snivelling child of around seven years old who had constant green slime hanging from a nostril which every now and again she would either sniff up so it would disappear back inside or be wiped away on her coat sleeve, was holding on to a battered old push-chair that seemed to be almost buried under a pile of carrier bags which constituted the rest of the family's luggage. From somewhere beneath the pile a baby of around a year old insisted on balling its head off.

The parents of this small tribe fared little better, shouting at the snivelling child not to wipe the dog's mess off her shoe on my front mat and screaming at the eldest two to 'shut the f..k up' for constantly moaning about S__ being a dump and wishing they could have been left at home. The father, dressed in a dirty pair of jeans and an even dirtier tee-shirt, announced that he was Arthur and his wife, wearing a sort of faded smock and with a fag dangling from her mouth, was Clara. They were expected, he informed me, as they had made a booking with the former owners and paid for a week, but they would consider staying for a fortnight if I could reduce the price a bit for the second week.

Horror of horrors! What could I have said? They did indeed have a crumpled up receipt, one that showed they had paid £20 per night for the lot of them, and which the previous owner seemed to have forgotten to mention to me, or hand over any money. However, this was a minor detail as I was now faced with this rabble.

Thinking as fast as I could, I told them we were fully booked for a second week, the bar was closed down and there was no longer a guest lounge. In a blind panic I even offered to refund their money, despite not having seen any of it, if they wanted to find somewhere else.

"No, mate," the father said, "we've tried all the others in the road before and they're always full. Besides, it's handy here for the pub and the betting shop, and the kids will be happy playing in your lounge if they don't want to go to the beach. Thought we had come to the wrong place what with it all being done up. You must be raking it in. Shame about the bar though. Anyway, we will get up to our room and see how it goes. We are all bursting for a slash and the baby needs changing."

I stood to one side and in disbelief watched as the rabble traipsed up the stairs, the push-chair scuffing my new wallpaper, and as the snivelling child, who by now had decided to do some deep mining up her other nostril, wiped off the spoils on the handrail as she followed on behind. For a moment I listened from the bottom of the stairs at them shouting and arguing amongst themselves, with presumably the snivelling child being the one jumping up and down on my new beds with glee, and no doubt with her shoes still on.

The mother appeared from the toilet on the stairs and shouted down to me, "I've left the baby's nappy on the floor in the bog, the previous geezer's wife used to put them in the twin-tub with the tea-towels and their own washing and then leave them out for me in the mornings."

Quick as a flash, I announced that I ran the guest house on my own so they would have to sort out their own washing at the local launderette. She turned on her heels and went back into her room, slamming the door loudly. Listening intently, I could hear her saying, ". . . and we have to do our own bleeding washing now! And who's that in the other room making the beds? Do you think they are queers?"

"Probably," came the reply from her husband. "They're everywhere now. You daren't turn round anymore without fear of getting shafted up the arse!"

This family appeared to have little finesse or social graces. Not ten minutes later they were all on the way out again, clattering down the stairs, off to the betting shop and then the pub before doing the pier I was told as they slammed the front door behind them.

Lance came downstairs and, not believing what was happening as we were not even open properly yet, said, "You can't let them stay, they are going to wreck the place!"

My worst nightmare was panning out in front of me. I had to get rid of them. But how?

In an attempt to console and un-burden myself, I telephoned Colin, one of my former colleagues at the undertakers, just to let him and all the others there know how I was getting on. They were so pleased to hear from me and wanted all the detail as the phone was passed from person to person around the mortuary. Naturally I mentioned the family from Hell that had just arrived, and that I was trying to think of a way of getting rid of them. Putting the phone down, I was pleased that I got in touch with them again, and for a brief while it took my mind off the problem in hand.

An hour later and the phone rang again. It was Colin announcing they were all on their way over to see me that evening after work. They would be staying the night this time and, providing they could park the hearse out the front again, they insisted it would not be a problem to get rid of my family. It would be great to see them all again, and just the right thing to lift my spirits, but wondered exactly what were they planning on saying to the family?

After explaining to Lance that my friends would be coming for the night, and revealing to him what my former occupation was, it mattered not a jot to him. Quite the reverse, he found it hilarious! I rushed next door to put *all fur coat and no knickers*, Cynthia, in the picture.

She had enthused at how well the place had come on in the past weeks and was nice about all the noise and activity. She had been happy to put up with it all because the improvements progressed at such a pace. Her only problem now was that she had noticed the family arrive earlier, and remembered them as staying there the previous two years running when it was absolute hell for them and the other neighbours what with the noise and the two eldest being seen at nights regularly drinking and having sex with all sorts in the back alley. She was sure they had been dealing in drugs too because of the frequent comings and goings of what appeared to be the dregs of the town.

Would I now upset her further by mentioning my former colleagues were paying another visit and wanted to leave the hearse parked outside again, this time all night? I was worried about it, but needlessly. As it was to rid us of the family, she was quite happy, and she even invited herself and her husband around later that night so they could meet everyone, and she could see what I had done to the inside of the house.

At five o'clock, the family from Hell came crashing in and bounded up the stairs, leaving a trail of sand and mud behind them on the hall carpet, along with a nice new cigarette burn. They had come back with carrier bags full of cans of lager and cheap bottles of wine. They were for the room, they told me, before announcing they, the parents, would be going out again around nine o'clock, once the two smallest children were asleep and the two elder ones had gone out for the night.

On seeing them back, my heart had sunk again. I had hoped they might have been washed away by a tidal wave or got run over by a bus, or at the very least have had a bout of amnesia and forgotten where they were staying. No such luck, unfortunately!

Joy of joys! Colin and the others arrived at six thirty. The hearse was parked outside and - yes! - they had brought me another load of fresh flowers. Most unusually, all the guys appeared quite muted as they filed into my lounge, each of them carrying armfuls of flowers. Apparently they had a plan, one to which I was asked to agree with anything that happened. I had always trusted them implicitly, so I readily agreed.

Charlie, who was always the moaner, especially about where he could or could not smoke in crematoriums, had been talking to Lance. They seemed to get on remarkably well. Anyway, I was asked to make tea for everyone and to leave my lounge door into the hall wedged open. Lance, they instructed to uncover my child's antique coffin that still served as a coffee table. This he did, and then began to busy himself by putting flowers all around the room as the guys brought more and more bunches in.

A beautiful white wreath with 'Toby' emblazoned in red flowers across the middle, Lance placed on top of the child's coffin, pulling off the card that said simply, 'Granddad'. Once satisfied with the arrangement, he disappeared off upstairs with Andrew and Tom, the two who always did the makeup on the deceased. I guessed it was for them to see his room on the top floor.

I can remember how chilly it became with both my lounge door and the front door wedged open. The draught had positively rattled my cup in the saucer, and as I sat there attempting to drink my tea, I was wondering what was going to happen next. Well, I did not have to wait long to find out. The parents, closely followed by the two eldest kids, gingerly came down the stairs and, aghast, looked into my lounge.

Charlie immediately took them to one side and asked, "Are you relations of the deceased child?"

"No," the father blurted out. "We are just here on holiday. What's happened?" His wife was stuffing a most revoltingly stained grey handkerchief to her mouth.

Turning to me, Charlie said, "Don't be upset, sir. I will explain. You sit down there, relax, and drink your tea. We will look after everything."

Charlie then went on to tell the family in hushed tones, and with great reverence, of how the family staying the previous week had illegally come into the country from Botswana with their youngest son suffering from Malaria, and how he had subsequently died in the family room upstairs. Whilst he was explaining all this, and following a quick briefing by Colin outside, from next door Cynthia and her husband arrived with tears in their eyes.

The family's two eldest were morbidly interested, coming out with comments such as, "Cool. Wow! Wicked!" and "Can we have a look in the coffin?" But by now the mother had become quite distraught. "We can't stay here, Arthur! It's horrible! It gives me the creeps!" she said.

Cynthia interjected and, in a magnificent pretence of sympathy, comfortingly said, "There, there, my dear. Don't let any of this spoil your holiday, you will have forgotten all about it by the morning. Your room is beautiful now, and you have nothing at all to worry about because the infectious diseases team from the hospital have been here all week disinfecting it. They've done Darryl's kitchen too, so you should not be worrying. All the worrying was done last week when the poor little lad could be heard screaming out in pain all night before he passed away. It was only this morning that the body was allowed to be brought down into the lounge.

"The little lad's parents will be here soon to see the coffin. Apparently they have a clean bill of health and are being released from the detention centre under licence. I know that Darryl plans to put them out of the way, on the floor above you, until they are deported back home, so you needn't worry, you will only ever see them at breakfast."

At this point, well blow me down if Andrew and Tom didn't walk back into the room and I had to look at them twice. A double-take. With them was a young lady in a scarf. It covered a great deal of her face, but a second more closer look made me realise it was Lance, and obviously Andrew and Tom had applied the makeup.

"Who's she?" asked the mother from Hell.

I explained to her that the young lady was a resident from the top floor. She was on release from the local psychiatric hospital in the charge of social services who had placed her here. Shortly after the hearse pulled up, she had been spotted climbing out of the window. Fortunately the driver, who had seen her, and his colleagues managed to race upstairs and get her back inside, but usually she was no trouble at all.

"Right, that's it! We're leaving now! Come on Arthur, and you kids. Upstairs and pack now! The sooner we're out of here the better," screamed the mother, with her two eldest loving every minute of it and wanting to stay. Little s…s!

"Oh, it is such a shame you've decided to go. You do realise I can't give you any money back, of course. You are cancelling your booking without any real reason," I told her, not that I had received any money. "I am so sorry to see you leave."

At that, they were all off upstairs, and within a few minutes all cascading down again with the pushchair bumping on every stair tread in their eagerness to get out. Once they had gone, we all had a fabulous evening. The drink flowed like water and Cynthia and her husband declared they hadn't had so much fun in years.

Later on, in private, as we prepared nourishment for our guests, Lance gradually admitted to me that he was a cross-dresser and would prefer to live in women's clothes all the time. He was not sure if he was gay and wondered if I minded. He would go if I did. Although somewhat disappointed that he was not sure about being gay, I decided I would not do anything to encourage him either way. He needed to make his own mind up on that one. I told him, of course I didn't mind. In spite of that uncertainty, he was such a great lad that I knew I was more than happy just to have him there. Selfish, I know.

Whilst we were all making merry, there was a knock at the door. It was the owners of the old people's home just up on the other side of the road. They had seen the hearse parked outside and called for a business card in case they were to fall out with their normal undertakers. That was a possibility because their commission seemed to be going down, they said. I invited them inside and the guys quickly obliged by providing them with their card, so soon we had yet another couple embroiled and enjoying our impromptu party where the family from Hell were frequently the cause for our laughter.

The guys told the visitors about my antecedents, and the couple suggested that perhaps, when they had one of their residents pass away, which happened quite often, for a fee, I could go over there and lay them out, as their own staff were squeamish about doing it. I knew that if it is not done within a few hours, rigor mortis sets in and if the person has died in the armchair it can be a devil of a job flattening them out, so appreciating another source of income I agreed, saying it was a good idea.

It was four in the morning before the owners of the rest home together with Cynthia and her husband finally departed and we all managed to crash out. Another day over, a real disaster averted, and I had loads of new friends.

How lucky was I?

April 11th

It was great having my former colleagues and friends staying over for a night last week, and I appreciated their invaluable help in getting rid of the family from Hell for me. They too had all enjoyed their trip and after breakfast distributed the flowers they had brought between Cynthia next door and the old people's rest home almost opposite me, leaving me with just a discreet few to decorate my hall.

I had to bin the wreath though. Dave, the builder, arrived just before they were leaving and shared an enjoyable pot of tea with them, afterwards even managing to persuade them to pick up his ladders from my yard and run them round to his house in the back of the hearse on their way home.

Lance was a star, helping me with the breakfast that morning. He had clearly enjoyed all the fun of the previous evening. We agreed that wearing whatever he liked was okay with me, just so long as there were no guests or visitors around. For the rest of the week, after helping me with making up the rooms, he spent a lot of time helping Dave make good the yard following the demolition of the outside loo and the building of my covered walkway from the kitchen door to my private bedroom door. Completely covered in, and looking every bit like a corridor, it was a grand job.

Having worked so well together, Dave offered Lance at least three days work a week. He is putting him on his books and going to train him to be a bricklayer. On the other two days, Lance said he would like to continue helping me run the guest house whilst he was staying with me, and if it was alright he did not even want to look for anywhere else at the moment. Of course, I agreed - it was a fabulous arrangement!

Slowly bookings started coming in, mainly being passed on from the guys I had gone to Blackpool with even though I know they are not all full themselves yet at the weekends. I decided to meet them all at The Freedom Tavern one evening a few days later when they had arranged to discuss getting a group started for gay hoteliers. On arriving I got myself a drink and then updated them on all that had happened, not forgetting to thank everyone for the bookings they had sent me. Before getting down to the business they had planned for the evening, we all settled down for a bit of a gossip first - doesn't everyone?

It transpires that whilst we were all away in Blackpool, Julian and Tristan were quite busy for the weekend. We guessed they had picked up a lot of the business that we had missed through being away, and it so happened that weekend had clashed with one of their Nudist Art Weekends. They had decided to capitalise on this as much as possible and so told as many rent boys as they knew that there could be a lot of business for them at their place that weekend.

Now it had always grieved Julian and Tristan that when one of their punters went off with one of these boys upstairs to the punter's room, for whatever reason, the boys, who were supposed to give Julian and Tristan ten percent of the take later on or at breakfast the next day, being boys, especially these boys, weren't always so forthcoming, or indeed forthright about the level of service they had provided and the amount earned.

To overcome this problem, Julian and Tristan decided to print a menu of services that the rent boys could provide on to individual cards with tick boxes and the prices. The guests could fill these out on arrival and make their payment in advance, so leaving the hosts to pass them on along with the money, less their ten percent, of course, to the allocated rent boys. They knew they had to tread carefully in designing the menus, just in case they fell into the wrong hands, so they went something like this:

Art Class Extras, booking on arrival, sorry no cheques.	Per Hour
Private sitting	£12.50
Brass Rubbing	£20.00
Canvas Blow Dry	£25.00
Penetrating Ink	£40.00
Water Mixing Techniques	£45.00
Class Discipline Techniques	£30.00
Brown and Yellow Sheeting	ask at reception

That Friday evening the guests had all arrived and Julian and Tristan were pleased with the numbers, and with the range of services ordered. The cards they duly gave out to the rent boys as they arrived, and strictly on a first come, first served basis - no pun intended. The evening started well, the bar was busy in expectation, the harp in the corner hadn't seen so many lemons pushed through it for the gin and tonics since New Years Eve, and those guests that were just voyeurs had taken their places naked at the easels ready to watch the first model perform. Suddenly all hell broke loose as two of the guests began to argue over which rent boy they wanted.

Each of them had hold of one of the boy's arms and was attempting to tug the lad away from the other. Meanwhile the rent boy that neither of them wanted was left standing there, card in hand. Bemused and offended, he was questioning what was wrong with him - apparently, he was a bit of a minger who usually slept rough on the promenade between tricks!

With all the pushing and shoving going on, the melee that ensued progressed through the lounge, scattering easels, stools, paper and pencils to the sound of ample rolls of naked flesh slapping against each other as people tried to get out of the way. In an attempt to pick up all that had been scattered, the voyeurs seemed to bend over all at once, the resulting sight resembling a host of lemon jellies fresh out of their moulds, all wobbling in unison.

The fracas then moved on out into the hallway where, with a hefty push from one of the aggrieved guys on the other, and with a swift movement of his hand on the door, he had the other one pushed outside on his own and the door slammed shut on him.

The elderly balding guy marooned on the street, dressed only in the lightest and shortest of white smocks with his blue-veined legs poking from beneath, pummelled on the door to be let in whilst screaming at the top of his voice, presumably to the boy inside, that the other guy had a much smaller donger than him and couldn't get it up if he tried! It was definitely the last time he would ever loan him his lube, he shouted.

Inside there was as much noise as there was outside as Tristan and Julian tried to wrestle the other guy away from keeping the door shut, and meanwhile back in the lounge, from behind the velvet drapes, a gaggle of elderly naked gentleman all with the top half of their meat and veg just visible over the window sill, were vociferously giving the man outside some encouragement.

This scene of pandemonium carried on for just a couple of minutes before the police arrived. They had been patrolling in the area when a complaint from a neighbour about all the noise had been relayed. Quick as a flash, the velvet curtains were yanked shut, the door was thrown open by Tristan, and naked bodies could be seen rushing along the hall and upstairs, with the guy from outside in his mad scramble to get back inside and up the stairs, stumbling and tumbling over, as if they were mooning to the officers arriving at the door.

The four police officers, all dressed in their riot gear, were greeted by a flushed Tristan who was trying to pull the door closed behind him. He explained that it was just a stag do that had got a bit out of hand, and apologised profusely.

That might have been the end of the matter, were he not to have been standing there dressed only in a large nappy held together by an even larger safety pin. Not satisfied, the officers insisted on going inside to check that everything was okay, and in spite of Tristan's protestations pushed past him and went into the lounge.

In their haste to get away upstairs, no-one had thought to switch off the television which continued to show a graphic porn video with the sound down. Julian immediately started rushing around in an attempt to straighten the room. He at least had his skimpy tight khaki shorts on, although as he was in the habit at these nudist art weekends of putting something large inside them and had no time to remove it, it could be seen teasingly hanging down just below the hem. Still it probably impressed the officers, who were trying to stifle their mirth.

One police officer picked up a menu from off the floor and proceeded to question Julian about the price structure, whilst at the same time studying some of the pencil drawings lying around. Another, on his haunches, thumbed through the pile of videos scattered on the floor.

However, it seems that Julian and Tristan may have got away with a severe lecture, at least for now, although they were informed the matter would be investigated further. The riot van outside with its blue lights flashing had alerted half the street, and once it had gone, a steady exodus of guests from the hotel could be seen.

Apparently Julian and Tristan have abandoned their art classes for the foreseeable future, and I never did get to see one of them for myself.

The evening in the pub just flew by, and not much was discussed about the new group except that we would indeed do it. I offered to look after the web side of things for the time being because Lance had told me his hobby, apart from the Steiff Bears, was computing. He was already going to sort out my internet connection when my new computer arrived the next week, so I thought why not get him to set it all up for us. After agreeing who was going to do what, and the date for another meeting, it was time to depart.

I did walk home past Julian and Tristan's place with the intention of seeing how they were, but the curtains were closed and all the lights were out. Whilst I do not agree with their lifestyle, I was concerned for them and felt sorry for the hassle and embarrassment they must have gone through. So I rang the doorbell.

Julian answered it and seemed genuinely pleased to see me, inviting me in. They both relayed the story, more or less word for word, as we had heard it at the pub. Clearly they were shocked at what had happened and had resolved to think of another idea to bring in the business. They wanted to know what I thought about cookery classes, as you could do a lot of things with a bit of pastry. Pottery was another option, if they could get hold of a kiln that would sit in the patio area at the back. I did reluctantly point out that both these ideas were particularly messy and perhaps they might like to think about running the guest house as just that, a guest house.

There was little business about at the moment, they were at pains to point out, and me refurbishing my place and opening up hadn't helped that situation. Further bad news was that Julian had lost his part-time job in London, and the café on the promenade didn't want any more cakes from them - whether this was because of the incident that weekend or the fact that sometimes Julian bought the cakes from Tesco's and unwrapped them pretending them to be his, I didn't know. Clearly they were having difficulties, but because of the late hour I had to make my excuses and leave for home. However I did promise to

return later in the week at a time when we could sit down
and discuss sensibly their ideas for the future.

May 1st

Another Bank Holiday weekend arrived and this time I was ready for it. All the bedrooms were prepared, and all the new crockery and cutlery set out ready for breakfast in the dining room. During the morning, Tristan and Julian called in to thank me for visiting them with my advice. They had taken it on board about the cookery and pottery classes, and the possible mess that this could make in their beautiful place, and instead decided to advertise special 'Spank Holiday Weekends' which they could do at any time.

They were thinking of advertising it as a place where all the smart-arses could come for a paddle. I wasn't too sure about it myself, but they were insistent they had hit on a winning formula and were quite excited about it, even demanding I should attend their first event. I don't think so, somehow.

A steady trickle of telephone bookings came in during the week and by Thursday afternoon I was fully booked for the Saturday, but just for the Saturday. They were all only for the one night, and it soon dawned on me that having accepted all these one night bookings I had lost out on any following calls that might be for two or more nights. Never mind, I thought, at least I was full for a night and that might just about cover my loan repayments and other outgoings for the week.

I wasn't over-enthusiastic about the booking for the group of fourteen girls, and I wondered how they would fit in. Would my place be of the right quality and style for them? I did explain to the woman making the booking that there was no bar. She had sounded refined, replying it would not be a problem as the young ladies may well have a drink out. It was one of the girl's birthday, and she was also getting married the following week.

The woman, who had sounded sweet, almost apologetic for disturbing me, divulged that all the young ladies worked together at a financial institution in the City of London. How nice, I thought. It would be brill to have some quality guests in.

A few more gay and straight couples and a group of guys coming for the football match were booked in the rest of the rooms, so I was looking forward to taking some real money that Saturday. Lance rushed around in the morning, vacuuming and dusting the rooms before changing out of his dress prior to the first ones arriving. It was the various couples who arrived first and they all seemed happy with their rooms and soon settled in. The gay guys commented on what a nice job I had made of the place as they went out to visit the bars. They turned out to be a group as well, but had all booked separately.

Then the group of girls arrived and it was great to see this long line of eager chattering young females queuing outside the door waiting as one by one I took their payments, issued them with their keys, and Lance showed them to their rooms.

The eleventh one to book in said, "Sorry, darling. Three of us couldn't make it."

"Who's paying for their room?" I asked.

"Well, we are all paying individually. It was the mother of one of those not coming who made the bookings, so I don't know, darling."

Damn! I could have let that room if I had known. Perhaps I should get one of those credit card machines that all the other hoteliers had, then I could take a deposit when someone books, I thought.

The group of guys here for the football match arrived in a mini-bus and I watched with some trepidation as they spewed out of it. Clearly they had all had one or two too many sherbets on the way here. It was a noisy check in, and I had to remind them about not disturbing the young ladies in the house. But at that it got even noisier, and some ribald and course remarks became part of their banter.

Two of the said ladies then chose that moment to appear at the top of the stairs, and it seemed they were more than happy to join in with the exchanges of some suggestive remarks, even proposing they all met up later that evening. It was an arrangement that rallied a loud cheer from the guys.

During the rest of the afternoon I could hear them all coming and going, but they seemed to be enjoying themselves and getting along noisily with each other, even the gay and straight couples in house, so I decided to try and relax whilst joyously counting the money I had taken. It was a strange feeling to suddenly have my house almost full with all these people, and I hoped I would be able to cope with it, especially the many breakfasts.

Strangely, by ten o'clock the house was deserted, and I sat wondering what time everyone would be coming back. Even Lance had gone out to experience the local transvestite club for the first time, and alone. He took a holdall with him as he was intending to change in the club's loo. Very brave.

I decided to stay up and wait for everyone to return, being much too hesitant to go to bed. Lance was the first one back, and couldn't stop talking, marvelling at all the people he had met and how fabulous they looked. He was definitely going back again sometime, he said, although he wasn't too happy about having to fend off so many invites and roving hands.

Around two-thirty in the morning, the bulk of the guests returned, almost as one enormous group. The guys and the girls all appeared to be intertwined, the girls in nurses' outfits with huge false boobs and fishnet stockings, the guys, mostly with no tops on, in shorts and huge black fuzzy wigs.

Save for a few, they were all amazingly drunk. A couple were retching and spewing up onto the pavement the kebabs they had eaten on the way back, to the amusement of the rest of the rabble. At one point I had to insist that the no entry sign, complete with its post, suggesting it had been pulled out of the ground, was left outside.

I then spent the next hour or so dashing upstairs, every few minutes it seemed, to remind them about the noise. The corridors were alive with the comings and goings as both the girls and the boys went from room to room, letting the doors slam shut behind them. I came to suspect there was a certain amount of hanky-panky going on. However by four o'clock the house became silent and the last group of gay guys returning went quietly to their rooms. It was off to bed for myself and Lance then, him up to his own room, but not before promising to be down again by seven-thirty to help me with the breakfasts.

Of course with all the excitement I could not sleep at all well. I was quite relieved when seven o'clock arrived and finally I could get up to prepare all those breakfasts. It wasn't long before I had ten tins of baked beans and ten tins of tomatoes gently simmering on the cooker. A mountain of eggs stood ready, and the bacon and sausages were slowly grilling. Four loaves of bread were by the three toasters and four electric kettles on standby. I resolved to get myself a water boiler very soon. With the huge pile of plates gently warming in the cooker, I was soon all prepared in the kitchen.

The dining room, Lance said, was fun to set with all my new individual jams and marmalades, packet sugars, salt, pepper, and sachets of brown and red sauces. Six cartons of orange juice and six litres of milk had been opened and poured into jugs, a selection of six different breakfast cereals opened up ready for the guests to help themselves, and flowers from earlier in the week placed around to decorate every table. Once the new music centre had been tuned to fill the room with Radio One at a discreet level, Lance went off upstairs knocking on every door to remind the occupants that breakfast was being served in the next fifteen minutes. In retrospect I suspect this perhaps wasn't one of his best ideas.

Before long I could hear toilets flushing, doors being opened and closed, people calling to each other, and then a steady stream of people came down into the dining room, all avidly talking and laughing about the previous night. Some, I might add, were scantily dressed. With Lance telling me how many as they arrived, I popped down the toasters, broke the right number of eggs into the frying pans, and filled enough tea and coffee pots almost at the same time. I frequently burnt my hands getting the plates out of the oven, but I was too panic-stricken by then to bother about it.

With the plates lined up on the work surface, I dished out a ladle-full of beans and tomatoes onto each one, a couple of sausages, some bacon, and then rushed to fill the kettles again, whilst at the same time trying to save the eggs from burning. During all this Lance was busy bringing back the dirty cereal bowls and squeezing past me to refill milk and orange juice jugs, not to mention several times rescuing the toast before it caught alight.

To say it was bedlam is an understatement. The sink area soon disappeared beneath a mountain of dirty crockery, with the floor becoming a skating rink from spilt oil, tomato juice, and the baked bean sauce that had dribbled from the serving ladle. The waste bin was overflowing with half-eaten toast, egg shells, and the remains of uneaten breakfasts scraped off the plates, whilst everywhere the surfaces were covered in bread crumbs and half-empty cartons of milk and orange juice.

In the middle of all this chaos the fire alarm went off, much to the amusement of the diners. It seems the frying pans beginning to smoke on the seriously oil-splattered cooker had set it off. Damn the toast, I had to stop everything whilst I ran to get the instruction book to learn how to silence it. Meanwhile Lance was reassuring everyone there was nothing to worry about, telling them it was only due to the chef setting light to his underwear in his rush to serve everyone. The Tart!

Amidst this theatre of mayhem, someone decided it

would be a good time to enquire about an ironing board and iron, and another couple appeared at the desk wanting to check out. The phone had started to ring, and just wouldn't stop, and suddenly I couldn't even remember what day it was anymore. Then blow me down if the doorbell didn't ring too! It was a guy who introduced himself as Raymond. I recognised him as coming from the hotel a few doors along the road, the one with private parking and a staggering front garden and patio.

Until now I had just acknowledged his friendly wave. He had called in to ask if he could borrow an egg as he was one short for his guests. Very kindly he suggested I should pay him a visit the following day for an afternoon drink. Now that was indeed kind of him, I thought, and eager to accept I gave him two eggs, just in case he dropped one on the way back.

Suffice to say, it came with great relief when the last diner had finished eating and left to go upstairs again, leaving the dining room looking as if a bomb had gone off there. Gradually, as we set about clearing everything up, the guests began to leave, all of them saying what a great time they had had, and how they would be returning again soon. I don't think so, I thought to myself. From now on it is definitely no groups, and no one-night bookings on Bank Holidays or Saturdays!

Lance had to leave in order to help Dave the builder who had a job that required finishing, even though it was a Sunday, and so I was left to sort out all the rooms on my own. Almost every room looked as if it had hosted the second world war, with the bedding scrunched up, some of it on the floor, and empty bottles and cans strewn around. The carpets were covered in glitter and feathers from the fancy hats bought on the promenade, the drawers half-open and food wrappers lying around everywhere.

Glasses could be found under beds or by the toilets, some still half-full of drink, and the curtains were either half-closed or tied in knots. Many of the toilets had not been flushed, several lights had been left on, and the stains on the furniture, presumably from drink, were hardly camouflaged by the full to overflowing ashtrays.

It took three sacks to clear away all the rubbish, and on every corridor a huge pile of laundry appeared as I stripped the beds. In spite of the disarray in every room, I soon had them cleaned up and put straight. Thank God, there had been no permanent damage. By the evening I had managed to make all the beds, in between loading the washing machine, emptying it into the dryer, and putting yet another load in to wash. Six loads it took before all the washing was done.

The ironing took nearly all of the following day. Afterwards, I decided to visit Raymond for a respite and a chat on his front patio. I found it a pleasant change to simply sit in the sun, peering through the foliage of his front borders and watch life go by. Raymond had been in S__ for many years and was gay himself, although you would never guess. He had a rather austere countenance on first meeting, but it soon became apparent he was rather soft, gentle and caring, in spite of his age. Clearly, in his day he must have been a real Adonis - you know, the sort that banged that big gong at the start of the Rank films.

Anyway, he seemed to know everything there was to know about the town, its residents and the many gay businesses. He was a mine of information on how to run a guest house and soon advised me on how to get a Pretty Damn Quick machine (otherwise known as a PDQ terminal) for processing credit cards. We got on like a house on fire, even more so when he showed me his Rolls Royce in the garage at the back of his property.

I enthused over the advance and retard levers on the steering wheel, the huge electrical control box under the dash and the separate switches to start it up. This was clearly his pride and joy, and he has promised to take me out for a spin in it one day.

It was such a welcome break, and a real chance to share experiences. Raymond had been a deep sea diver, a coal miner, and for a short spell, when circuses still had live animals, a lion tamer - until being gored one day in the leg. He showed me the scars that were still evident. After that, he had done some plate-spinning as a side act, but this soon wore away some of his hair so he gave it up to become a prizefighter at a fun fair.

When that lost him some of his front teeth, he gave that up too and decided to settle down with his own guest house. That was over twenty years ago. He did just briefly try his hand at farming, but found he could not keep up with the speed of the cows when trying to bring them back to the cowshed in the evenings.

The guest house he had now was a modest establishment, but the rooms which he showed me round were spotless and furnished amply without any unnecessary frills or adornments. His guests were for the most part, he said, old and young regulars that came several times a year, every year. Clearly there was a lot to learn from this guy.

So it has transpired that our social soirées have now become a regular daily activity once work is done.

May 24th

Last week was great, with a full house but for one room for the first time. A great learning curve too, to boot. What with that and all the advice from Raymond, who has a guest house a little further along the road, I feel I am getting the hang of it at last.

The computer arrived on Monday and Lance took charge in getting it set up. What a performance! I was happy to leave it to him, listening as he wrapped himself in wires, plugging everything in and occasionally swearing in his attempt to get on line (whatever that is). The set-up has made my lounge and empire look professional, especially since the PDQ machine arrived at the end of the week as well.

I tried it out by putting my own credit card in and charging myself £110. Fabulous! It worked perfectly, debiting my personal account and crediting my business account. I tried it a few more times to make sure. What a wonderful wheeze to top up my business account! Now all I need to do is work out how to do refunds.

The first task Lance undertook, once the computer was working, was to look at my website. Sure enough, when my web address was put into a search engine, up it came, the first entry on the first page. Wonderful, I thought, until Lance informed me that my one page site was ghastly, and that anyone just typing, 'Gay Guest House S__' into Google, as they probably might, resulted in it not appearing until dozens of pages after the first one.

What a bummer! Anyway, he said that he would build me a new site, set up some better meta tags, and do all the submissions himself. Of course, I hadn't a clue what he was talking about so I just left him to get on with it. The bonus is he likes doing it so much, he has already started work on a site for the new gay group we proposed whilst at the pub last time.

On Tuesday night the owner of the rest home nearby, Celia, who had popped over to ask my friends from the mortuary for a business card, came to see me again. She asked if I could sort out one of her gentlemen residents for her. Apparently he had expired whilst sitting on the loo. She was at pains to explain that her partner, an SRN, was out at the chemists collecting a packet of Senakot, a laxative, for the resident as the liquid paraffin clearly had not been working of late. Unfortunately, the resident had probably strained much too hard, passing on to the next world before the SRN could return with it.

Happy to oblige, I trundled across the road with Celia to the rest home where sure enough, the resident, quite cold now, was sitting on the loo with his trousers and pants around his ankles, and a strained expression on his face. He was clearly very much a goner. With Celia's help, I managed to get him off and out of the loo and into his bedroom without too much hassle, and without any of the other residents noticing. Unfortunately, it is quite normal with corpses for the bowels to open naturally, and what the poor guy was trying to achieve earlier happened just as we got him near to the bed.

The smell, and the escaping wind from the bowels and lungs from being wrestled around, was appalling. Celia clearly began to feel more than a little nauseous, but it didn't take long for me to strip the guy and clean him and the floor up, leaving her free to frantically roll cigarettes and keep a constant cloud of smoke going in an attempt to mask the smell. She was insistent that I stayed until her partner Sonja, who I had yet to meet, returned from the chemist.

This was interesting, I thought. I had stumbled across my first meeting with a lesbian couple, and they were running a rest home. One, which Celia revealed, where they preferred to take in only gay male clients nearing the end of their days because they were much easier and friendlier to deal with. All the time she was talking, she patiently and with great precision whittled away at a three-metre lump of wood. She explained to me that she was trying to fashion it into a four-inch wedge for her office door.

She did all the maintenance on the premises herself, and the administration, she said, whilst her partner looked after the residents, and the all-male part-time carers, along with seeing to the cooking and cleaning. Clearly Celia had a lot of DIY skills, I discovered. Apart from being just a competent carpenter, she was the sort who would dip screws into pots of grease before screwing them in, just in case they should need to be unscrewed again years later. With her grey hair tied up in a bun, her roll-up cigarette dangling from her lips and her boiler suit with every conceivable tool hanging from the belt, she did look very much the part. This was certainly no lady to be on the wrong side of.

I had noticed her before, at the roadside, but not thought any more of it, when she appeared to be struggling to put a front bumper on her performance car, with bits of engine lying all around and a huge tool box open on the pavement. With the emancipation of women, one expects and is used to seeing them taking on the heavy industrial work that was previously just the male preserve, and why not?

Within the hour, Celia's partner Sonja returned. She was upset to learn of Albert's demise whilst she was away shopping, but being a lady of some beauty and obvious class, immediately threw herself into making me welcome. From the kitchen she produced, and offered around, a plate of fairy cakes she had baked earlier. We sat around for a couple of hours whilst the two of them gave me some insights of running a care home for the elderly, explaining how important it was to get the residents out into the fresh air every day, and to not forget to bring them back in again for tea or if it should start to rain.

Care had to be taken not to mix up their false teeth, which were put into the dishwasher every night, and they definitely could not allow the residents to watch too much mucky television. That upset the night staff who had to fend them off when putting them to bed.

Apparently both of them had been married. Celia, a defiant non-drinker and a former devout Presbyterian, to a professional Irish accordion player who used to tour the pubs - the marriage not lasting more than a couple of years whilst Sonja had married in Austria, where she was born, to a former Russian KGB agent and had two children now living in East Germany with children of their own. Both women loved to visit them at every opportunity, Celia especially as she felt at home being welcomed with open arms by the naval dockyard workers with whom she would spend many a happy hour discussing the mechanics of ships' diesel engines.

Sonja had eventually left her husband, as he regularly practised his interrogation techniques on her. That in itself hadn't been too bad, but being manacled to the wall in the cellar was, and had been the last straw. By a happy coincidence she had met Celia, who happened to be on holiday in Berlin and at the time was foraging amongst the rubble for a memento piece of the Berlin wall whilst it was being demolished. Since then they had not looked back and were clearly devoted to each other.

Their rest home was smart and practical, the whole place looking like an Ikea showroom with clean unfussy furniture in light teak. Their office, every bit to compete, included the smartest and most efficient library, with every piece of paper documented, recorded, filed away and accounted for. Not only were they going to pay me for my assistance, but they asked me to contact my former colleagues at the undertakers to handle the arrangements for their resident. So, it was a good result all round - except, of course, for their resident.

The girls, as I now refer to them, were also were great friends with Raymond, and they spoke too of being good friends with another couple of gay guys not far away, Danny and Sidney, who for their great sense of humour and hospitality were affectionately known as the Chuckle Brothers. They had run a small but prestigious guest house for many years, specialising in providing haute cuisine evening meals. One of them, a former head chef on a cruise liner, The Star of Venice, was now fully immersed in local politics, avidly reading the daily papers cover to cover. He would entertain his guests and friends for hours with his pronouncements on putting the country to rights. His younger partner lectured part-time at the local university on astrophysics, and could regularly be seen driving about in a classic, lovingly and fully restored, bright pink Reliant Robin, a sort of large pram on wheels.

What an area! A real gay community encompassing so many former entrepreneurs, and such a myriad of skills, with all of the people helping each other, and I appeared to have been welcomed into it. It would be fantastic to arrange a party for them all.

Well, that was my week, a good one, but what a performance it is now with all this smoking ban lark, isn't it? I'm alright, as since abandoning any idea of a bar I have turned the Connaught Room into my private lounge. However, I expect my guests will now be throwing cigarette ends down the loos and the sink overflows, only to be left floating in the former and blocking the latter, and that's apart from the increased risk of fire.

Never mind, I'm off tonight to check out the pubs and clubs to see what, if any, effect the ban is having on them. One positive thing about everyone standing outside smoking is that it will save any punters having to buy the drinks first before chatting up the rent boys!

June 25th

I took myself around the town Monday night to a few pubs and clubs to see just how they were coping with the new Smoking Regulations, and what an entertaining evening it turned out to be. Every establishment had a group of smokers standing outside the doorways, all huddled together under building canopies in an attempt to stay dry or light another cigarette.

Pushing my way through into the Capricious Man Bar, I found it was disturbingly quiet, just three people sitting quietly talking in one corner. Then I noticed a sign directing people to the smoking area, a freshly put together space down some steel stairs in the back yard. Built around the home of a barrel, gas bottle and dustbins with great imagination was a lean-to made of see through corrugated plastic.

This covered half the area which had been furnished with a few wooden barbeque table sets and lanterns decorating the rough brick walls. Every few feet along the walls were doors, each with its own label such as pump room, sewage outflow, gas chamber, electricity switch room etcetera, and in between every door was a wall-mounted cigarette box. The noise of the air-conditioning machines and beer chiller motors added yet more to the scene. It may only have been a small concreted area, I might add, but it was full of atmosphere. I couldn't help thinking that some rough trade clubs would spend literally many thousands of pounds to achieve this look, and yet here was the real thing.

One of those amongst us decided on a count of the

people in the different areas. There were thirteen of us, and in the bar, missing out on all the noticeable and enjoyable camaraderie found in the smokers' area where everyone was talking to everyone else, there were just two people. This whole new smoking scene is worthy of a visit, even for non-smokers.

Next I visited the Stag Bar, which is a tiny, dingy sort of place. The barman there was all alone polishing the counter, then the shelves, then the counter again, then arranging the crisps, and then carefully turning all the bottle labels in the chiller to face the front. He was looking miserable. I guessed he was probably a smoker himself. In the time it took to have just one drink, a few more people arrived, but they were only the staff setting up the disco. For some reason, they all huddled around a vacuum cleaner in great discussion. It looked rather pathetic.

Off I went again to yet another pub, a busier one this time, but not as busy as one would have expected. After all, it had been popular, and there was the drag show to come a bit later. The DJ was attempting to breathe some life into the customers, but they all sat around the tables looking bemused and cheated of the atmosphere. Occasionally, a couple would get up and leave to stand around outside the door on the street, joining others there, including some of the bar staff and bouncers, all having a quick cigarette.

Next, I was going to try the pub on the corner, but a peek in through the large windows told me it was completely empty apart from the bouncer who was peering back out. I thought better of going inside, deciding to just stand there and smoke a cigarette before going on to the last venue on my list, which was just around the corner. This is a large bar that has the luxury of a decked sun terrace.

From inside the bar, I was able to look out at the terrace and watch the rain sweeping across the decking. Thoughtfully, someone had left one umbrella open above a table out there, but that was being tossed about in the wind and throwing rivers of water down onto the backs of the few smokers brave enough to try cramming underneath it to get a fix.

Just like the other bars and clubs, inside it was sterile and subdued. It looked like the non-smokers had taken over the world, and there was certainly lots of room for them in this part of it. I suspected that it was with great amusement they watched the unclean amongst us gagging for a fag, and braving the indignity of standing around in the elements.

Still, I was glad to be a part of these particular lepers; at least they were enjoying themselves, unlike the prissy, supercilious few left sitting around in the huge deserted open spaces of the bars, all sipping away slowly on their half-pints and bottles of mineral water.

Now that Lance has set up my computer and given me a few hours of instruction on how to search the web, I have had many a happy hour exploring, only to be castigated by him a few days later for filling up the computer with links to all the mucky websites and a surprising number of pop-ups advertising casinos and porn sites. These just seem to appear out of nowhere, even when the browser is not open, and are a nightmare to get rid of. Delete one and another ten appear behind it.

Not to be distracted, I came across a gay site that promised to find the man of my dreams. All I had to do was fill out a comprehensive online form with all my personal details and provide a picture, which I got off my website, and tell them exactly what I was looking for in a partner. I could then search the database myself, and my details would also be available for the other members of the site which apparently numbers hundreds of thousands. Honesty is the best policy, I decided, if I was to be serious about a long term partner, so I put exactly how old I was, what my interests were, suggesting that I was of average looks and build, and was a self-sufficient business person with my own guest house in S__.

What was I looking for? Well, I said he would have to be good looking, of course, slim, clean, the same age or even younger than me, self-sufficient with his own income or working possibly in a professional capacity at least for the moment, interested in the Arts and Classical Music, enjoy country walks and entertaining at home and so on. Once the the form was filled, and my credit card debited the £45 for the supreme platinum service, hey presto, I was in and able to look at all the other members and their ads. It took my breath away, pages and pages of pictures of half-naked and completely naked guys from eighteen to ninety, with quite explicit descriptions of what they wanted. I must say, the vast majority seemed to just want sex of one kind or another, generally another. There were baby fetishists, lads looking for sugar daddies, rubber and vinyl enthusiasts, some complete with pictures of them naked in gas masks. There were a great many ads that I thought of as looking similar to mine, and with pictures that they would not be ashamed to show their grandmother. Somewhat cautiously, I started sending short emails to register my interest and to see if they would respond. I had already decided not to reply to any that had a naked picture or had described their most personal measurements.

The next day my inbox on the site had over three hundred emails, all seemingly desperate to meet me. With great excitement, I spent the whole day looking in fine detail at all the profiles and reading the most incredible array of offers of all sorts of sexual exploits, including quite a few who wanted to come on the next train down. Some had attachments of explicit pictures of themselves.

Amongst all of them, there were just ten that were quite appealing and to which I duly responded by suggesting that they telephone me and arrange to come for a visit in the near future. I am now hoping that some actually will, and I shall let you know just how I get on. It is all rather exciting.

After reading these emails, I added to my profile what it was that I was not looking for, to try and thin out some of the most unsuitable. This amounted to several paragraphs, but still the emails kept on coming.

Lance, when I told him what I had been up to, was somewhat critical of the whole thing and I began to wonder if he was a bit worried about his own situation. I went to some lengths to assure him that his position, staying with me, was secure no matter how long it took him to find a home and work of his own, if indeed that was what he wanted to do. However, it transpired that he was more concerned for my safety. He has insisted that if anyone comes to see me, he wants to be around to vet them. Beautiful lad! He has since added spam filters, virus checkers and put my machine on some sort of parental control which he says he won't lift until I know what I am doing.

I did notice that he can get to his Tranny sites though, and without any problem. Bit of a cheek, but he does know what he is doing and I suppose it is only sensible, although I've had to draw the line at him wanting to vet my emails before I have read them myself.

The environmental health man called again this week and was extremely complimentary about my guest house, passing it with flying colours this time. With him he brought a large, quite ridiculous folder that is impossible to shut without a lot of fumbling, and the contents often dropping out all over the floor. Called *Safer Food, Better Business*, this is especially for me, and so he spent the next hour explaining what it was about. It was the new regulations in food handling, and had to be completed daily.

There was a pictorial section that looked similar to a children's early learning big print book detailing instructions on all the procedures and management controls that had to be in place, along with lots of check boxes to tick and personal cooking processes, cleaning schedules and so on, all to be written out.

I worked my way through it and think I have got the hang of it at last. The bonus is that there is a day to day diary section which has to be completed each and every day, and this will be useful for keeping track of any respondents from the web contacts I hope to amass, as well as somewhere to put my advance guest bookings in. What a boon it would be to anyone doing the horses every day!

It's the last week of June and the bookings are definitely a bit slim, so I have been trying some of these online booking websites. Looking through them, I picked out twenty-five free ones and five that you have to pay for. They all seem to be so positive that their sites are viewed by hundreds of potential guests each week, all eager to book accommodation, that it seems silly not to join them. Especially as they virtually all will put my advertisement on and link it to my webpage. I can't lose can I?

I have decided to be listed on a selection of gay and straight sites, to get as much coverage as possible. I am beginning to need it now, so I consider the £480 I've paid out, along with the fee sites, will be a good investment in the end. The last attack on getting business was to put a box advertisement in four of the most popular gay magazines, although the cost of these combined adverts did make me wince a bit. But hey, it will be nice to see my place in print, and I look forward to all the bookings that will come flooding in. I can pass the overspill on to my new found friends. I'm surprised they haven't done this themselves already. I shall have to tell them about it when we next meet.

July 6th

What a funny old week it was - it must have been National Tight-Arse Week! It all started when I answered a telephone call from someone wanting to know about the prices.

"How much for one night?" they asked.

Politely, I told the caller the price per person, per night. The next question was, "What would it be for two nights?"

Quick as a flash I responded with, "Twice as much as it is for one night."

"Oh, no discount for two nights then?" they asked. Then "Would it be extra for two people in the same room?"

"Double what it is for one," I told them.

Possibly this was more than they could comprehend as they said they needed to think about it. They would get back to me. That evening, a well-dressed foreign gentleman, accompanied by his wife and three children, knocked at the door to ask the cost of a one-night stay. Having told him the cost of a family room and then invited them to look at the room first, they trooped upstairs for an inspection. Once inside the room, the wife immediately began to pull the bedcovers back and I had to explain to her that the beds were actually empty and that she would quite easily have noticed if someone had been asleep in any of them.

At that, one of the children wandered off into the en-suite facilities and began peeing into the toilet, so it came with some relief when the gentleman, nodding in agreement with his wife and saying it was a lovely room, told me they would stay. He would be right down to pay me.

Down he came within five minutes, but only to suggest that they should have a twenty percent discount as they were vegetarians. It was usual, he told me. Cereals, toast, and fish was all they would be requiring for breakfast. I duly declined. Fifteen percent then, he insisted, and it would be a deal. Once again I declined, but not deterred, he spent the next five minutes attempting to haggle with me. It would be rude of me to repeat my final answer here, but perhaps it is suffice to say that they left quite quickly.

On Friday, an elderly gentleman appeared at the door wanting a room for at least a week, maybe longer. He explained that he was working evenings in the bigger hotels as an entertainer, and asked if he could pay for just the first night initially. As he would be getting paid later that evening, he would pay me for the rest of the week the following morning. It sounded okay until morning arrived and he announced, politely and apologetically, that the manager where he was working had gone sick and he would not be getting paid for three days. Nevertheless, he would see me right, he insisted, even offering to get me any cigarettes or tobacco I might want to purchase cheaply from someone at the hotel where he was employed. I only had to give him the money for them first and he would bring them back later. Another offer I felt it prudent to decline, and so he too was ushered on his way. I did feel a bit harsh and mean until I went up to clean the room. Judging by the amount of empty cans and cigarette ends in saucers, he had been nowhere at all the previous night.

Saturday, and another couple rang the doorbell. They

needed accommodation for two in a twin room for one night. There was no quibble over the price so they paid there and then. That done, the man straightaway walked to the front door, leaned out, and shouted up the street. Moments later two children appeared. One was about five and the other taller than the parents.

"Who are these, then?" I asked.

"It's alright mate, they're our kids and they sleep with us," he said, and in the blinking of an eye started to proceed upstairs. Without further ado, I snatched the keys back out of his hand and returned the money, the whole tribe being shown straight back out of the door, but not without some very ripe language erupting from all of them.

In the end, it turned out to be quite a reasonable week with lots of nice ordinary people happily enjoying themselves. Well, that is apart from the woman who received a parking ticket outside and expected me to pay for it. Apparently it was my fault because there were yellow lines outside that I hadn't told her about.

During the week, I found the time to pop up the road to see Julian and Tristan who told me all about their first 'Spank Holiday Weekend'. They had advertised it in a couple of the leather and sadomasochism gay magazines, and this had resulted in the whole place being booked by one S&M group from London. Not only was it for two nights, but they had paid the total amount in advance.

The person making the booking had asked if they were familiar with S&M and wondered if they would be relaxed about anything that went on over the weekend, which they would also be welcom to join in, if they so wished. Well,

Tristan and Julian had always thought of themselves as totally uninhibited and willing to give anything a try, so they confirmed they were quite happy with any of the arrangements, especially after they were told that some of the group would be bringing their young slaves with them for further training.

In readiness for this first event, Julian travelled to London and purchased a whole raft of canes, whips, paddles, leather cuffs and belts, and a myriad of other assorted restraints complete with chains and padlocks. Clearly they prepared for the weekend with great excitement and anticipation, even covering the lounge furniture in black sheets, attaching restraints to the easels left-over from the Nudist Art Weekends, and screwing huge hooks to suspend people from into the top and bottom of several door frames.

When the group arrived, Julian and Tristan could not believe their eyes. In their words, they were so butch and rough, mostly bearded, overweight, and all of them in full leathers, but there were half-a-dozen or so cute looking lads too. Apparently, these were the slaves. In no time at all the bar was thronging, with the horse play becoming a little rough at times and the glass coffee table getting broken, Julian explained, but as they had expected some horseplay, they consoled themselves with all the money from the booking.

Not long into the evening, Julian and Tristan had a chance to get away from behind the bar at the invitation of some of the guys who by now were in various states of undress, with the smell of leather and the cracking sounds of paddles on buttocks filling the air. A few of the members being slapped, mostly the younger and clean-shaven of them dangling from the doorways or tied over the settee and armchairs, were muffling their screams with the handkerchiefs that had been stuck in their mouths, and Julian and Tristan were invited to join in with the whipping. They were getting into the swing of it when it was suggested they might like to have a go at trying out the manacles for themselves. With a promise to be gentle, they were soon both straddled across the settee and firmly tied down with chains and handcuffs. It all seemed such great fun as they were stripped and started to receive some gentle caning. Yes, of course it stung, they admitted, but they did find it erotic when combined with the activities of the others performing around them.

Some of the younger ones, those who had been introduced as slaves, were instructed to take over the bar and to perform all manner of other services for the rest of the group, fair enough as everything was being paid for, and this went on for a few hours. Later, the slaves were ordered into the kitchen and prepared supper for everyone, with Julian and Tristan not objecting one bit, they being by now well into the party, even if stinging a little. Still locked in the manacles, they were sat upright by the slaves whilst they managed something to eat and drink along with the rest of the group.

Supper over, the leader of the group announced they were all going out for a few drinks, leaving the slaves to clear up. They could have some fun of their own with hoteliers, he said, and with that they departed, leaving Julian and Tristan thinking it all sounded like fun.

The half-a-dozen slaves left behind soon had the

clearing and washing-up done as instructed, and returned to pay attention to Julian and Tristan. The lads, who had up to now been extremely subservient, became almost demonic in discussing what they should do to them. Dragging Tristan over the settee again they manacled his wrists to his ankles, and then turned to Julian. Pushing him up against the harp, they tied his wrists and ankles to the top and bottom whilst one of them pulled his private parts through the strings and put an enormous stainless steel ring around them, making it impossible for their prisoner to withdraw.

At first, the two hosts were happy to go along with it all, until the full leather face masks with zips over the eye and mouth pieces were put on them. They could see nothing, and just had to imagine what was coming next. Needless to say, they got a right good spanking, and unsurprisingly the nipple-clamps hurt. Over the next hour or so, all manner of items, including ice cubes, were inserted into all sorts of places, and no matter how hard they tried, they could not get free. Attempting to shout out, even in pain, was an impossibility.

A couple of hours of this passed by before the rest of the group returned and, much to the relief of Julian and Tristan, they were released and the masks removed, but any respite was only short-lived. Ignoring their protests, within minutes they were both laid out full-length on the floor, manacled together this time, and tied between the bottom of the door frame and the sofa. A tray of drinks was put next to them which they could barely get enough slack from the chains to reach, a blanket loosely thrown over them, and two large empty saucepans for obvious use placed nearby. After wishing them both goodnight, the group went off up to bed, closing the door behind them.

At the time, they thought this was part of the game, one which they were thoroughly fed up with by then and that had left them extremely sore in the most intimate of places. But alas, no-one returned, and they were left there all night.

It was not until nine in the morning that some of the slaves came down and started to wash them, still keeping them manacled, with the others, if you please, making breakfast for everyone.

Things had gone much too far for Julian and Tristan by now and they complained bitterly to the group's leader, insisting that they had had quite enough. He only laughed, reminding them that when the booking was made, they'd agreed to go along with anything that happened, and up until this point they had clearly been enjoying themselves. They were required to honour the booking completely so they would not be released until the group's departure time the following morning.

And so it was, the poor dears had another twenty-four hours of much the same treatment, occasionally having the face masks and manacles put on, to be escorted to the loo, and then it was back to another round of degradation and pain inflicted by the slaves.

On the morning of the departure, true to their word, the group released them, and they were congratulated on providing such wonderful sport. It was even suggested that they might like to become members.

What bliss it was, Julian declared, once they had all left. Never before had they been so tormented, brutalized and humiliated. However, on reflection, they concluded that maybe it wasn't all that bad, as they had made some real money, with the guys paying for everything they had consumed and even coughing-up for the broken coffee table. The slaves had cleaned the rooms, found clean linen and made the beds, and vacuumed everywhere.

Given the rewards, Julian and Tristan were seriously considering whether or not they should go for it again. They asked me if I would be willing to help them out if they did, so leaving them to just serve behind the bar.

Perhaps not, I told them. I was aware that they hadn't sat down once throughout all the time we were talking.

July 17th

It has been a quiet week, and my free grace period where I didn't have to pay for the loan obtained by mortgaging my property is now up. To my horror, I now have to find £800 a month. Just where this is going to come from panics me like hell. The business is certainly not able to support it along with all the other running costs, such as business rates, domestic rates, electricity, gas and just plain old living.

Everyone is telling me this is the worst year for business ever, and what with the weather, along with the recent increase in interest rates adding to the fewer numbers of guests visiting S__ and maybe even the smoking ban, who knows, it is all looking pretty grim.

To compound it all, Lance, my gorgeous, undecided, new cross-dressing friend and resident, has met another cross-dresser, a butch-looking lorry driver from Plymouth, and announced that they would be looking for a home to share together down that way. He is planning on going back with the guy on his lorry in two weeks time. I knew he would go at some stage, but so soon is a great shock. I will certainly miss his help around the place, quite apart from his computer skills, although he has promised to try and get me up to speed and teach me as much as possible before he leaves. It is going to be empty around the place without him.

Despite all the advertising I have paid for on websites and in gay magazines, the phone is still not ringing. It is so silent that some days I pick it up just to reassure myself it is actually working. The only calls coming in seem to be from people wanting to sell me something, or to change my service provider. On Fridays and Saturdays a few people call, but only to book for the one night over the weekend. It is all quite disheartening.

And still it is raining.

Cynthia, my neighbour, has placed a notice under her vacancy sign that says, *Alternative Genders Catered For*. Poor dear! Even she says she is feeling the pinch. The neighbours on the other side, those I met when moving in and who saw me running naked to my outside loo, told me they are not taking in guests anymore and have now got jobs in the local DIY superstore. They have been fantastic neighbours and friends, with an extended family who seem to visit them almost daily, the sons and daughters being parents themselves, children with boy friends and girl friends, and grandchildren.

When they invited me in to tell me about their new occupations, it was like something out of Eastenders. The whole family was talking, rushing up and down stairs, occasionally arguing with each other, or on the telephone, whilst another daughter and her husband were rocking their crying baby to sleep, and all the time my neighbours were getting out the tea or another whisky or gin and tonic, and occasionally interjecting to quell an argument with some good old common sense before turning back to describe their new careers. What a family! So in tune and caring about each other.

They told me that when they first moved into the area and opened their B&B, after both being laid off from the munitions factory at Woolwich, it was swamped every year, all summer long, with guests staying for two weeks at a time. They were the days when they could charge for salt, pepper, and even a towel, with the guests being thrown out every day after breakfast and not allowed to return until supper time. The good old days, they called them. I'm not so sure about that, I thought.

Over the years, they had noticed the decline in the number of attractions for visitors, and apathy from the council in maintaining the infrastructure or enticing conference business. They had allowed what were once some prestigious listed buildings to fall into disrepair and decline, or had sold them off. There was a feeling that all the councillors, who across the parties had been in office for years, whatever party happened to be in office at the time, had it sown up either with back-handers or agreements to maintain the status quo on planning and development. It seemed that all they wanted was to be able to get through to retirement without too much work or grief. The last thing they appeared to want was to bring in professionals and start in any serious way on some sort of regeneration, apart from that which central government obliged them to do, like sea defences. In fairness, the council did pay huge sums of money, millions of pounds, employing lots of different quangos with an ever burgeoning office staff to produce a myriad of reports that they could discuss over the years. But at the end of the day, this was a huge smoke screen that would allow them to keep jogging along, drawing generous salaries.

Obviously, some things had been done, like painting almost every road with yellow lines, putting up parking meters, employing a small army of traffic wardens and building even more council offices. It seemed to my neighbours that the only significant new business brought to the town was by the gay commuinity, new clubs and pubs and hotels that were generally regarded as a much better option than the older, run down guest houses and hotels which had turned into stag and hen venues, or into hostels for foreign workers. They said the town was now full of waifs and strays from the rest of the country. What was once a premier seaside resort now resembled a war zone at the weekends, with the stag and hen parties taking over the town, and the local yobs and vandals terrorising the residential areas.

Anyway, they were hoping to sell up one day and move abroad. They had a daughter who had married a Turk, and eventually they wanted to join them in Istanbul to help out in their date packing and distribution plant.

These were great neighbours, often seen tending the flower boxes along the front of their property. Every Monday they would be in the yard assisting each other in putting the washing through the mangle and hanging it out. A fabulous family. What a shame it is that they might be going. Who might I get as new neighbours? I have to hope that none of this will happen for years to come.

The news did not get any better.

On Wednesday, I popped down to the Freedom Tavern and all the talk was of Andre and Sami who had operated Andre's Hotel for the past five years. They too had been caught up in the downturn of visitors, in spite of spending thousands of pounds on renovations. Because they were bigger than most, they had to take in groups from time to time, and no matter how careful they were in vetting them, they would regularly have damage to clear up. They had dispensed with their staff years ago, running it on their own, having to stay awake all night over the weekends to cope with the comings and goings of the occasional few drunken, noisy guests who slipped through the net. Now they had sold up, but for twenty percent less than they wanted, and bought a house locally. Deciding to work from home, Sami was setting up an internet underwear business, importing from the Far East, while Andre was to retire altogether and live off of his pension from a former lifetime of packing golf balls.

They weren't the only ones. Two more hotels came onto the market this week, one of them being leasehold and wanting a lot of work done to comply with current legislation.

It was generally agreed by everyone there that this would indeed be a difficult season.

Even Raymond, who I had a drink with most afternoons, could not offer too much cheer telling me that whilst he ticked along quite nicely with his regulars, they were all getting older, and every now and then the news would filter through that one of them had expired. New regulars seemed to be much sparser these days. He was hoping his plans to put in a stair lift might keep his current regulars still coming, apart from being useful when he had to make up the rooms himself.

To save costs, he had recently turned the stopcock almost off for the hot water to the rooms in the hope that guests would not fill the sinks or spend too long in the showers. He had already put in an outside power point for guests to plug in their wheelchairs, and now he was considering decking his front area and selling some of his copious amounts of flowers to passers by. If he could get the planning approved, he was also thinking about selling teas and coffees, and perhaps a few daily papers from this decked area. After all, he had the equipment; it just needed dragging out in the mornings after breakfast.

Hearing all this, I am now seriously thinking of what cutbacks I can make myself. Raymond's water management idea seems worth a thought, and perhaps I could purchase a job lot of electric wheelchairs myself. I don't think that financial advisor who arranged my mortgage had my best interests at heart after all, judging by the money I now need to find. I could probably get some work at the local undertakers to help out, but that would take me away from my business. It is, however, a route I may have to consider.

On Friday the telephone rang and the caller announced he was from a television company. He wanted to know if I would be willing to take part in a new series they were about to make. It is going to be about a season in the life of a guest house which specialises in taking groups of young men on pre-release holidays from detention centres. This was a new scheme to be tried, and the film company proposed to pay for all the rooms for the whole of next season, along with a lump sum in advance, on signing the contract and allowing them in over the next couple of months to do any slight modifications that were needed to accommodate the lighting and camera teams.

There was nothing on the books, so I agreed. It is already arranged that some members of the production team will come to see me next week to discuss details.

All very exciting. In fact, it could be a lifesaver!

July 18th

Monday, I was up like a lark. The person who spoke to me on the telephone last week about making a television series called again to tell me they were due to arrive that day at eleven. Hastily, Lance and I double-checked every room was in pristine condition and opened all the windows and doors to blow through the awful smells left behind from a myriad of colognes and after shaves that seem to linger forever.

Fortunately, what guests there were for the Saturday had all gone home on Sunday morning, so we had been able to get all the housekeeping done by the end of the day.

Right on time, the television people arrived - six of them in two taxis from the station. Peering through the curtains, Lance and I watched them as they stood around on the pavement glancing up at the roof. One of them was taking photographs of the outside of the building from every conceivable angle, whilst the others were in a huddle, deep in discussion, occasionally looking and pointing up and down the road.

Eventually, they rang the doorbell and I hurried to let them in. On opening the door, I noticed the net curtains were twitching over the road, and Cynthia, next door, had decided it was a good time to busy herself with mopping down her front steps.

Directing them all to my dining room, whilst Lance went to put the kettle on and find some biscuits, I was in awe at the friendly but professional approach of the group. With no prevarication, they got straight down to business. The offer was as I was told on the telephone last week, full payment for all the rooms for the rest of this season, and again for the whole of next season. The first payment would be advanced within the next two weeks. In return, I would have to look after the proposed guests as I normally would. It was important, they explained to me, that no-one in the area knew that the guests were on a pre-release holiday from a detention centre.

There would only be six at a time and they would always be accompanied by two officers from the relevant detention centre. None of them would be sex offenders or violent, I was assured. Phew! That was a relief, presuming they were referring to the inmates! Apparently, once rooms had been allocated to the lads and the two officers, all the rest of the rooms would be used up by the film crew.

Naturally there would be some modifications and changes made to accommodate all the cameras and lighting equipment, I was told. Possibly they might need to scruff-up the place just a tad for realism, but this would be up to the artistic director. Any changes made would, of course, be rectified by them at the end of next season.

They would take sole charge of the whole of the premises, assuming complete responsibility, so I would have no worries at all. It sounded great, and I could not wait to sign the agreement, which thoughtfully had already been prepared. After an hour or so of them looking over the property, and all agreeing what a wonderful place it was, they departed telling me that a small production team would be arriving later on in the week to make detailed plans and arrangements. I should have a couple of rooms ready for them to leave their equipment in.

The production team duly arrived on the Thursday.

There was the director and two assistants, an artistic director, the set accountant with yet another assistant, a senior cameraman and another two assistants, a first and second grip - and would I not like to get a grip on one of those! - a best boy, who happened to be as ugly as sin, a set designer and at least four other un- identified guys armed with machines. They began by checking my lighting and electrics, and measured every nook and cranny. Every now and again they would tap the walls, muttering to each other, and I could hear one of them say something like, "That will have to go," or "We can pull that down to get through here," and then they would scribble away madly in the huge notebooks that each of them carried.

After nearly all day of suffering them tramping around my place, they called me for a further meeting to discuss their needs for when the filming starts. It was a bit of a shock. They will have to knock down my backyard wall in order to get a crew catering van and an electricity generator in, and they intend to put up steel girders across both the dining room and the lounge to accommodate their lighting and cameras. A number of cables will also need to be fitted, and these will run along the ceilings, up the stairs, through the corridors and into each of the guests' rooms for more lighting and cameras. They propose putting my dining room and lounge furniture into storage, thus enabling them to use some older furniture and a pool table supplied by their props department, so it looks like the only living area left for me will be my basement bedroom. The good news is, because of something to do with Equity or the like, the crew will be completely catering for themselves by using the catering van parked in the yard.

Anyway, they want to have the first group in to make a pilot film within the next three weeks, before going full-steam ahead at the start of next season. I'm finding it all a bit of a rush. I was hoping to just lie about and watch them setting the place up for the rest of the year. Still, it is only for a week, so it shouldn't be too bad.

With Lance shortly going off with his new-found friend, I had been hoping my profile on the dating site would have produced more response. Perhaps my log in name, *darrylfromsouth,* is a bit confusing. I may need to think of some other way to attract a partner. After all, I should soon have a lot more time on my hands.

I managed to get to see Julian and Tristan during the week and tell them the news, except I omitted mentioning the sort of guests it was being filmed, just saying they were young men on outward bound course holidays. Julian and Tristan became excited and wondered if they could help me in the kitchen, or with the cleaning of the rooms, if I got too busy when the filming started proper next season. They even offered to sleep over if necessary. How kind they are, I thought.

You have to hand it to these two guys - not literally, of course! - they have decided that the S & M scene was a bit too heavy-going for them, so, still smarting a bit, they have thought up another new idea. This would involve much less work and drama than running the Nudist Art Weekends, as well as being much safer. They are thinking along the lines of offering *Holistic Touch Weekends.* These would be, they pointed out, a great draw to the less dress-conscious, or even the desperately shy or the particularly unattractive. They could come along for a weekend where they, with care and respect, were allowed to fondle each other, and the hosts, in a refined and gentle way, with the rules being that no items of clothing were ever to be removed or opened, at least not in the public areas. Tristan and Julian thought they could quite easily get it all going by encouraging the guests to have a fondle as they arrived, and reminding them they would always be around to be fondled at any time, although groping would be out of the question.

They were currently researching where to advertise this new service for maximum impact. They emphasised that the wording would have to be discreet. Maybe, they thought, something along the lines of suggesting these were holistic touch weekends for men only where they could get to know each other spiritually via the energies transmitted through their hands. They could even charge more for the spiritual angle, and guessed it might appeal to all sorts of groups such as gay older stamp collectors, train spotters, lonely hearts clubs and Masonic Lodges.

With this in mind, they were looking for the names of the magazines these groups might read, and thought perhaps that putting a notice in the reading rooms of various libraries around London might be worth the day out!

Over the last couple of weeks they hadn't fared too well business-wise and had soon spent all the money from their last event. Now they had to consider selling the harp in order to pay their rates this month. Last weekend Julian spent time late at night trolling along the sea front, and under the pier, to see if he could attract anyone that might not have managed to find a hotel for the night. He had returned quite dejected after all he got were offers from others to give him a service and, adding insult to injury, they had wanted him to pay. He had come to the conclusion the area was definitely going downhill.

July 19th

After all the running around with the film guys last week it was another fairly quiet weekend, but I was not too disappointed as it at least allowed me time to recover a tad. I was reinvigorated enough to spend some time visiting my friends in the Freedom Tavern again, this time for a hastily called meeting. The usual gang were there, Patrick and Dave who had the Dandelion guest house just a dozen or so doors from me, Andrew and Kelly who ran the Pastel Hotel, John who, on his own, had the Adventure Holiday Flats, and Gregory and Daniel.

Gregory had once been a fighter pilot, having been called up just after the last war. He had met Daniel, purely by chance, in a cottage local to Exeter Prison. Daniel had just been discharged from the prison, having served a month there for refusing to pay a fine for busking around Torquay. According to Gregory, he was a mean harmonica player with a voice like an angel. At the time Gregory had recently left the air-force and, still a young man, opened a fancy sandwich bar in the centre of Torquay, just up from the bay and opposite the turning to Meadfoot Beach. Apparently, business was not that good, but knowing Gregory with his upper class background and gastronomic prowess, that was probably due to him trying to knock out caviar and smoked salmon sandwiches to the plebs on their holidays. However, the upshot of it was that Gregory and Daniel hit it off, and in just a few months they had bought a guest house not far from S__ station. All this this was nearly twenty years ago, and at that time they were one of only three gay guest houses in the town. They became extremely busy.

A large-framed, portly gentleman, well over 6 foot tall, Gregory could best be described as gruff, off hand and outspoken. He had a short temper but an extremely dry sense of humour that was not always apparent. Catch him on a good day, and he could be fabulously entertaining with a wealth of life history to call on. On a bad one, he would be seen to snarl openly at guests who could nor deport or behave themselves accordingly.

He had always been the Chef and Manager of their establishment, The Thespian, with Daniel being the general dog's body who would do all the housekeeping, maintenance, and waiting at tables. All the same, they did work remarkably well together. Although there were rarely any conversations about life, they had obviously always been very much in love and that had grown stronger as the years had passed. Daniel had even managed to drag his partner along to the Registry Office last year to go through the Civil Partnership. Gregory, huffing and puffing about the nonsense of it all, but nevertheless still spending an inordinate amount of money on presents for Daniel and secretly providing a reception, continues to this day to remind everyone about the cost.

Those potential guests who actually made it through the door of The Thespian for an interview prior to being allowed to book in were often directed to see the rooms first, and alone. In the meantime Gregory would think long and hard about whether or not he wanted them. It could be their dress, deportment, manners, quality of luggage or he might just not like them, so often when the potential guests returned back down the stairs it was not unusual for him to, point blank, say to them, "No, I don't like you. You will have to find somewhere else. Goodbye!" Should they complain, he would at times be known to retort with, "Piss off!", and that would straightaway end the conversation.

For those that did make it through as guests, after listening to the quite strict rules of the house being explained to them, they were indeed pleased to be in one of the best and most modern establishments in S__ at that time. All the rooms were en-suite - quite a novelty twenty years ago - and furnished without any expense being spared. Gregory's breakfasts were more of a feast than a morning snack. The extensive menu included the usual bacon and eggs etcetera, but also kippers, salmon, grapefruit, a selection of fresh fruits, mushrooms, ham, cold meats and vegetables - and all would be prepared individually to order. Guests were told that they could have any quantity of whatever items they wished for, however there was just one rule: if they left any, they would summarily be asked to leave, and not just the dining room but to vacate altogether, with the comment from Gregory, "Please don't come back again," ringing in their ears.

They used to do evening meals too in those days, again another gastronomic feast with a number of choices for starters, main course, sweet, a huge selection of cheeses, biscuits and fresh fruit to follow. The meals usually consisted of five or six courses, but the same rules applied as at breakfast.

Nowadays, they rarely let their rooms. Gregory was feeling his age and Daniel had managed to find a position working for the local government. Gregory once explained to me that as he got older, the strain of dealing with the variety of guests and cooking for them was costing him far too much in whisky. Apparently, after cooking and serving a guest, he would have a tot of whisky and, with another guest to serve, it would be another tot of whisky. It would not be unusual to pass by his window following breakfast on a busy weekend to see him lurching from table to table in his attempt to clear up and reset the room in readiness for the next meal.

After a short nap, it would be off to the shops for him, an expedition that would inevitably involve a quick lager or three at the local bar, and then back to start once again on the cooking. Prior to each season, he would order eighteen cases of whisky from the corner shop to see him through, but now he was having a well deserved retirement and gradually converting his property back into a home again.

Back to the Freedom Tavern.

We were joined by Sandra and Tracy, who had the lesbian-only hotel, Vibrations, and their neighbours Karen and Julie, who took just about anyone in their guest house, The Sun Kissed Villa. Before we could get started, along came Raymond with a rather cute younger man who he introduced as his partner, Rodney. He's kept him quiet, I thought! Explaining that Rodney actually lived with his parents in the Midlands and had a good job in a Safari Park, I discovered that this was where they had met each other. Raymond would often get his old Roller out and go to see the lions there as they would bring back memories of him working in the circus as a lion tamer in his youth. Rodney could only stay with Raymond for the occasional weekends and holidays. He was a nice sort of rotund guy who told me his main hobby was shopping. If he had a chance, in-between helping Raymond with the room changes, the painting and decorating, and the laundry and cleaning, after preparing the evening meals he would be off to the shops with his best friend in S__, Sonja from the rest home.

This now explained the enormous amount of modern ornaments and knick-knacks that festooned Raymond's lounge. Every time Rodney went back home, he left behind another vase, clock, lamp or some labour-saving device for the kitchen, all bought for Raymond at bargain prices. He did have one fetish and that was for designer bags, of which he had several dozen. Raymond found them useful at times to move earth or bricks around in the garden, and naturally threw them away after use in the hope that Rodney would never notice. He never did!

Celia and Sonja had arrived with Raymond too, but stopped at the door to chat to those who smoked. They appeared to know everyone there. Celia rolled, deliberately and precisely, a cigarette. Puffing on it, whilst at the same time listening carefully to what was being said, she looked down knowledgably, nodding from time to time whilst examining the quality, or lack of it, in the fitting of the entrance doors to the frame. She tutted to herself.

The last to arrive were Danny and Sydney, affectionately known as the Chuckle Brothers. They apologised for being late saying it was due to the problem of finding a parking space for their bright pink Robin Reliant. Eventually, they had managed to park in an empty shopping trolley bay belonging to the supermarket around the corner which had now closed. It was at least under cover, and as a bit of a bonus they had also been able to tie the long chain for the trolleys around their bumper.

By now, an hour had already passed with everyone swapping gossip, getting drinks and rearranging the furniture so that we could all sit in a huge semi-circle. The meeting got off to a fine start with Patrick, as he had thought of the idea first, taking charge and outlining some of the basics. He suggested it should be a social group where everyone, including any newcomers, could get to know each other, share their experiences and pass on tips, as well as being a route to finding the best suppliers and tradesmen we all need from time to time. It was suggested, and generally agreed, that a regular bi-weekly social be mounted by each of the members in turn at their own places. In addition to making new friends in a secure and closed environment, for those with a bar it would be a chance for them to add to their income. Perhaps a raffle could be held to go towards the new group's expenditure. Members could bring in old tat given to them by their guests and foist it onto someone unlucky enough to win it.

Making me feel quite important, Patrick mentioned that I had a basic website set up ready for the group. I didn't tell them it was Lance, about to leave me, who had made it! He went on to ask if someone might like to volunteer to take it over. Perhaps we ought to have some sort of working group, a committee, he suggested, with someone to look after the accounts like a treasurer, and maybe a sort of secretary that could take notes and write things down for the records. A chairman and even a vice-chairman might be needed, and he threw that open for everyone to respond.

For a while there was a silence, nobody wanting to be seen to be too keen, until Patrick said that he should be the chairman himself. Someone immediately asked why and said it should be voted on. Patrick appeared to become a bit miffed at that - after all, it was his idea. Celia mumbled something about her doing all the paperwork for the nursing home, so she wouldn't mind acting as secretary and keeping any minutes, however they would either need to supply her with a suitable notebook and a pen or provide her with an allowance. She had some care plans from the NHS and felt sure these could be adapted and made into some sort of mission statement for the group.

Her partner, Sonja, added that she could get a copy of the constitution from the hospital trust where she worked, and that Celia might possibly be able to convert that to suit the groups aims. It began to sound professional and grand so everyone agreed.

John, from the New Adventure Holiday Flats, suggested he might like to look after the finance as for many years he had worked at a Post Office counter in Wales and was used to handling large amounts of money. He had only left the job because of a muddle with the stamps when they stopped printing the price on them. He was, he explained, colour blind, but had no problems at all with notes and coins. Again everyone agreed.

Danny and Sydney, in unison, piped up that they could look after the website. They had already been researching just how it all worked. Sydney, who of course lectured in astrophysics at the local university, promptly produced and distributed to everyone a thirty-seven page document complete with twelve pages of graphs and flow charts on the numbers and dynamics of websites saying it was all a question of 0s and 1s in computer geek stuff - it just needed the right numbers in the right order. He could even make pictures that moved about on the page for us! Everyone thumbed through the heavy document and to a man, nobody understood a word of it, so we all nodded our approval for the Chuckle Brothers to take over the website.

This still left the decision to be made of who would be the chairman. Gregory, who by now had dropped off to sleep and was quietly snoring, suddenly awoke with a start and bellowed out, "What's going on? I've been to more interesting church services! Can't we just get on with it?" Well, that was enough for someone from the back to immediately suggest Gregory should be the chairman. Before you knew it, a vote was taken and, much to his horror, we were all were congratulating him on his new position. In the end he didn't mind, thinking there would be nothing much to do, and so with that decided, he got up and left, saying he had to go to bed.

By this time we all were gagging for another drink, and some for a smoke and a stretch of the legs. Everyone was happy that the nucleus for S__'s new gay group was at last sorted, it being agreed that the rest of us would be on the committee. Further, it had also been decided that the group should be called SOS for Gays. With all this settled, it was back to the bar for more drinks, and within the hour everyone was quietly pissed.

Patrick seemed to take it all rather badly, picking up his pile of paperwork and saying, "Stuff the lot of you. You will have all the suicidal and depressed gays descending on you anyway." I can't help thinking he may be right, and perhaps I ought to bring it up at the next meeting. That is in a week's time at Vibrations.

It seemed to be a momentous evening as well as being great fun. Certainly, we all seemed to enjoy the company of each other and definitely new friends were made. The girls did tend to stick together but were nonetheless friendly. It would be nice to see more involvement from them, but give it time.

Walking back with Andrew and Kelly, we discussed the idea of badges for everyone on the committee, perhaps gold on white, and they could even be embossed to hang around the neck from a rainbow scarf for when we met up or went out together to the pubs and clubs. With them, we might even be able to get into the venues free, who knows? Andrew said he was already thinking about asking for a discount from the egg man and the laundry bloke.

July 26th

This last week has seen the lovely Lance leaving with his new friend, the butch lorry driver who is also a cross-dresser. Now I have no one to drool over anymore. Lance had brought him round once, in his drag. He was a thick-set guy who sported a beehive blonde wig. I could clearly see the hairs from his chest peeking through a sort of lace top to the dress he wore, and the bright red lipstick, just a bit smudged at the corners and with hints of it on his teeth, gave him a rather frightening smile. His choice of a short leopard-skin dress did tend to show his varicose veins even through the thick stockings, and I could not help noticing that the zips had burst open on his off-white snow boots so that white laces, which he informed me had been dipped in that glitter stuff, were now cleverly holding them together.

In fairness, I did congratulate him on his look, but asked why he had not shaved off some of the visible hair, especially from the back of his huge hands with the pork sausage-shaped fingers. He told me he was reluctant to because of the flack he might get back in the transport depot. Shame!

As they left I got the idea that Lance wasn't so keen on going off with this guy after all, but he had committed himself to it. He was one who clearly enjoyed the freedom to explore and had done that by helping me with all the renovations. Now, he was disappointed he would not be around to see the filming.

The young lad we had picked up on our journey back from Blackpool Pride with his huge rucksack and an even bigger hold-all was leaving me, the person he had chosen to stay with for a while, but now with a mountain of dresses, shoes, wigs and make up bags. It was a sad moment. With lots of hugs, and promises to come straight back if things did not work out, I hoisted him up into the cab of the lorry and watched as he was driven away. I do hope it works out for him.

Some of the film company crew arrived early in the week and I was given a nice cheque to cover payment for the rest of the season. The generous proportions of the cheque allowed me to immediately pay all my commitments for the next six months. At least now I shall have no worries about paying my debts for a while, and anything else I can earn in the meantime, perhaps by way of sneaking the odd guest in if the film crew aren't around, will be my spending money.

As the week went on, more and more film crew arrived. Along with them came all the set builders and technicians, and this created an enormous amount of interest from the neighbours, especially when some of my new furniture was taken out and old dilapidated replacements brought in. The wall separating my yard from the back alley was demolished and, after an hour or so of a lot of shouting, pushing and shoving, the crew's catering trailer was finally squeezed into the yard, but only just!

Inside the property the workmen knocked holes through the lounge wall into the dining room and erected two huge girders. From these hung mountains of camera and lighting equipment. At one point, in a panic, I rushed to see the set director after noticing the guys in the bedrooms were writing graffiti all over my new wallpaper and were even tearing bits of it away from the corners. Others were using a paint spray can to age the window frames and my nice white ceilings.

The set director pointed me in the direction of the set accountant who, rather curtly I thought, explained it was all in the contract I had signed, but I should not worry as it also stipulated they would put everything back exactly as they had found it. He assured me every part of the premises had been filmed prior to them wrecking it, and he even handed me a copy for my own reference. The old tart then asked me to stay out of the way of the film crew, telling me I would be summoned if or when I was required. Now whenever I walk around, some queen will tut and ask me not to for fear of mucking up the set, so all I can do is retire to my bedroom in the cellar - which I have had to fill with all the things I don't want them getting their hands on, including my antique child's coffin with the porn mags inside. Never mind, I continue to remind myself, I have the money and it will all be put back right in the end. I might as well enjoy it. At least I can still use the front lounge for a few days to have a cup of tea.

The telephone has not stopped ringing with locals wanting to know what is going on and, as I have been instructed by the film company, I have had to lie by telling them that it is all to do with the production of one of those DIY makeover series. I can't help noticing that Cynthia next door is dressed-up to the nines every day now, and that Celia and Sonja, who have the rest home on the other side of the road, are wheeling their residents out daily to the front of their property to take the sun where they can watch what is going on. All the wheelchairs look as if they have had a makeover too, with polished chrome wheels and spotless black plastic armrests.

The excitement didn't last long before the old scroat who has the guest house directly opposite me, the one who spends her life peeking out from behind net curtains for possible guests who, should she spot one, will be seen rushing out onto the pavement and almost dragging them towards her door, complained to some local business group about all the activity and noise in the road, saying it was disturbing her guests and lowering the tone of the area.

It was not long before I received a visit from the chairperson of this group, The S__ Urban Business and Residents Association, accompanied by the secretary. The chairperson, a Belinda Parsons no less (I have seen her in the local paper) apparently knows and gets on well with all the bigwigs in the town hall, and she also chairs several tourism-type groups. A keen and dedicated kind of person, she has even been seen to help push-start the odd coach with a problem in the bus garage. She is an elegant, well-dressed woman in her late thirties with an electric vibrancy, a vivacious smile and a personality to match. Leaning forward, as if to divulge a confidence, she explained that the person who had complained was one of those who never did anything for the association other than turn up occasionally at a meeting to complain about the bins not being emptied on time, or about men blatantly holding hands in the street, and always demanding to know what the association was doing about getting more guests for her.

"Don't worry about it at all, Darryl," Belinda said, after

hearing my explanation for the filming. "Quite apart from showing what could be done to these old properties with some DIY, I'm interested in just what a great boost this could be for tourism here."

Naturally, she wanted to meet the film director and the producer, and to be shown around. Happily, I introduced her to them, and whilst she was having her tour, the secretary of this association, Donald Duckworthy - what were his parents thinking of? - told me that Belinda, like all the members of the association, was a business owner. She had run a successful tourist caravan site on the old gasworks ground behind the fun fair until most of it was destroyed by fire after one of the holidaymakers had, against all the rules, started a barbeque. Fortunately, with the insurance payout she had been able to buy a large hotel on the seafront. Now she just leases it out, so giving her more time to spend on her various projects and her husband, a self-employed steel-erector and golfing fanatic.

"You may remember seeing in the papers and on television," Donald went on to say, "one of Belinda's great crusades a couple of years ago when she wanted the council to stop removing the whelk and cockle stalls from along the sea front."

He explained that the council, in their wisdom, were at that time removing these stalls in order to comply with EEC directives about contamination. The weight and descriptions of a portion of whelks, winkles, muscles, eels, shrimps and cockles etcetera also left much to be desired by the EEC. However this type of seafood had been bought here for decades, first by the holidaymakers from London and the crowds that arrived in their charabancs from the hop fields of Kent, and later by tourists of a much wider origin. Seafood had always been a great draw for S__, providing much employment and colour. People would come here to buy a few bottles of beer then pick up a plate of whelks on the front before putting knotted handkerchiefs on their heads and spending the afternoon lazing around in deckchairs on the beach until the pubs reopened.

Belinda had drawn the attention of the media to the loss of all this to the resort and the resultant effect it was having on local businesses in general. An article she wrote for the local paper was syndicated and soon the national press took it on board too, along with several television news programmes. The upshot of all this was that this quickly became news all around the world, and Belinda found herself having to spend a whole day either on the promenade or sitting in a deckchair on the beach whilst news teams from around the globe jostled to hear her story and filmed her tucking into a plate of whelks.

By the end of the day, and positively green from the many takes and retakes which had resulted in her eating enough whelks to last a lifetime, she had provided an enormous publicity stunt for S__. Since then, she has continued to work tirelessly for the town, pushing to smarten it up and to bring in new businesses. Her latest campaign was for a new mega-conference centre and amusement park complex.

I learned that Donald was formerly an entertainer on the London stage, but had been the secretary of this group since it started many years ago. He and his partner, Arthur, ran the Fell Climbers Hostel. On seeing my smile, he went on to explain that they mostly took in the normal holidaymakers. The choice of name had been deliberate and was used to advertise in the Fell Walkers Gazette as an alternative place to come for the older fell walkers who could not do the hills anymore, and for a while it had seemed to work quite well.

The man was a consummate reader and also a bit of an intellectual, collecting over the years a vast library of newspapers and magazines that filled almost two of his bedrooms and the cellar. Ask him anything and he would have the answer. A person of routine, he could be seen at exactly the same time every morning and evening walking his dog, one that from a distance resembled a small donkey.

On finishing her tour, and inviting the senior personnel of the film crew to a garden party next Sunday along with me and my friends Raymond and Robin, Belinda took her leave with Donald, promising to ensure that S__ would get as much publicity for the accommodation owners as she could muster. As she left, I felt that it was like closing the door on a whirlwind!

A few hours later, Julian and Tristan arrived, just to be nosey, but nevertheless they were welcome. As I could not let them upstairs, they stayed glued to their seats by the open lounge door. With big smiles and limp handshakes they spoke to everyone from the film crew as they passed by, ooh-ing and ah-ing and finding everything said by the crew, however trivial, to be outrageously funny, amusing or fantastically interesting. Rather cheekily too, I thought, they didn't waste a moment in promoting their own place, stating the obvious that is was for 'friends of Dorothy'.

They told me the fondling weekend had turned out to be a major flop. No one had booked, and now even more desperate for some income, they were thinking of trying a butt plug weekend. It transpires that there are quite a few people they know, and they feel there must be others too, who like to wear these accessories all the time. They already had a few themselves in various sizes, so they could assist by helping the guests try out different sizes and shapes. What they must do, they insisted, was to ensure that a piece of string was always securely threaded through to avoid them getting lost. That had happened to Julian some years ago, and all the doctors and nurses from the A&E department had stood around in obvious mirth to watch it being removed. It was just so embarrassing, he complained. I pointed out that if their guests were naked during these 'fittings' and were themselves of the more overweight type, there could, at the slightest hint of flatulence, or when someone bent over, perhaps to pick something up, be a potential problem with ricocheting butt plugs. They considered that momentarily then agreed they might need to give this idea more thought.

Julian, ever so casually, then suggested that with all the camera and lighting equipment now in my place, they knew of someone who dabbled in the making of porn films. This person was always on the lookout for new locations and would probably jump at the chance of being able to film indoors. He had no lighting equipment of his own and usually shot all his material in the woods around Billericay. This was fine during the summer, but he had a lot of trouble finding actors willing to strip off and perform from autumn onwards. In December and January it was absolutely impossible. Tristan felt that, if I was interested, they could talk to the guy and perhaps get me a small part in a film, and maybe some small amount of money for allowing him to use the equipment upstairs. It would have to be at the weekends though, when the film crew had gone home, of course.

I could see that they were intently looking for any sign of interest from me in my expression - you know, like the car salesman who nods to himself to encourage you to do likewise when asking you a question. Anyway, I now knew the real reason for my friends' visit, and I felt that, were I to agree to their suggestions, it could be a nice little earner for them. Not wishing to be too dismissive of the idea, I just as equally and casually suggested that they might like to loan me one of these films, and if after viewing it I was the slightest bit interested, I would think about giving them a call.

Now, though, I have to prepare for next week when the first bunch of pre-release lads with the two prison officers arrive for the pilot filming.

I must get a haircut.

July 30th

Monday morning and I was up at five to check the rooms for the six young men and their warders. On instructions, it was to be three to a room and the two warders in a twin room. The rooms looked ghastly by now, having been seriously scuffed-up by the set designer for effect, but they were at least ready.

An hour later and the film crew were busy hanging lights and setting up cameras with cables running everywhere. The kitchen became a busy thoroughfare for the crew as they went back and forth to the catering van for their meals and endless tea breaks. I wondered just how I was expected to serve a breakfast to the special guests with all the traffic, but then to get me out of everyone's way it was agreed that, as this would not be a feature of the film, the catering van would prepare the meals for me and all I had to do was run them through to the dining room. A fabulous arrangement, and free too!

I had been well briefed as to where I was to stand whilst booking them in, and had several rehearsals with some of the crew in how I was to show them to their rooms so as not to spoil the camera angles. I was even given a short script to learn on what I was to say to them on their arrival.

At midday, a plain green mini-van arrived at the front. I knew it must be my guests as a loud cheer erupted when the door was opened. Out they all leapt.

"Bit of a shit hole," one of them shouted to the others clambering out.

"Yeah, what a dump!" exclaimed another.

"Thought it was supposed to be a proper hotel. Hope

it's got an effing bar," another one said.

"Right you lot! Enough of that! Get inside now or we shall go straight back," one of the minders commanded.

The minders, fortunately, were both dressed in civilian clothes with just a small HMP logo on their blue-striped shirts.

"Miserable old c---t," muttered another lad as he pushed past me standing at the door, ready to greet them all.

The last of the lads, on his way in, noticed Cynthia next door, done up to the nines again and polishing the railings outside her place whilst intently watching this rabble coming in.

"Ullo darling, watch yur doing tonight then?" he called across to her with a wink and a cheeky smile.

Cynthia turned on her heels and fled back indoors, as one of the minders took the lad by the arm and pulled him past me and straight through into the dining room from where I could hear him being given a severe lecture.

The routine check-in that was expected, and that I had rehearsed, went out of the window as the other minder, still at the door with the lads discussing their movements for the day, took all the room keys from my hand and decided it was he who would show them up to their rooms. So up they all trooped, dragging their bags clumsily against my hallway wall as they climbed the stairs, with me following on behind.

"In you go," he ordered the first three lads, beckoning them into the first treble room, and then similarly to the other two into the other. That done, he leaned over the balcony and yelled down for the other lad to get his "arse upstairs, sharpish, now!" With them all in their rooms, he reminded them about not smoking or drinking on the premises, or to use any bad language, none of which would be tolerated. "Bo....ks!" came a retort from one of the rooms.

I had hoped for a better class of morons. These did seem a tad uncouth and I was already feeling nervous, but I consoled myself that they had their minders with them.

Shouting out that the lads should assemble in the dining room for refreshments in thirty minutes, the minders disappeared into their own room. One then popped his head back around the door and said, "Don't worry about coming up here again, Darryl. We will keep the little buggers under control, you take it easy. Just organize some tea and coffee with a few biscuits in the dining room for half an hour, if you can."

Well, this wasn't part of the plan, so off I went to see the film director to ask if I could get the refreshments from the catering van out in the back yard. He was hastily adjusting cameras and lights.

"Yes," he replied, "give them anything they ask for, it's all going just great."

The camera crew, which had been holed-up in a room on the top floor watching the event on monitors whilst controlling all the cameras and sound from a mixer panel, thought it was good television so far. One of them came to tell me to sit in on the dining room briefing to be given to the lads, and then to leave the minders to look after them. I would not be needed again until breakfast the next morning. Suits me, I thought.

Out at the catering van I requested, "Tea, coffee and

biscuits for nine, thank you. Oh, and one of those cream cakes too, please." Then, as I didn't see why I should leave myself out, I went on, "Better make it two of those ham sandwiches and a couple of doughnuts as well."

I quickly popped the additional items down into my bedroom for later. After all, I had been told to get anything that was wanted.

Down they all came into the dining room with the minders close behind, so I sat with the tea and biscuits to listen to the minders giving them the rules for their stay.

- *No alcohol on the premises*
- *Keep away from the pubs*
- *No visits to the betting shops*
- *No picking up ladies of the night (didn't mention men though!)*
- *Back by ten*
- *No drugs*
- *Make their own beds and keep their rooms clean (it gets better, I thought!)*
- *Do not travel out of the area.*

With that, they were all given twenty pounds each for the day, apparently from what they had saved from allowances whilst in the detention centre, and told to bugger off and stay out of trouble.

With a cheer, and the noise of my chairs suddenly being pushed back and cast aside, they all made for the door with great excitement as they left to explore the town. As soon as the last of the boys had gone through the door, the minders stated that, after an hour's paperwork, they would be going off to the pub for the afternoon. They would leave me their mobile phone number for emergencies.

After all that work up, it went surprisingly well, and as they had all gone out for the day, it meant that I had absolutely nothing to do until breakfast the following morning, and even then I wouldn't have to cook it!

A little later, the film director decided to hold a meeting to congratulate all the crew on the great footage and to plan the action for when the lads returned. Then he dispatched a mobile film crew to see if they could spot any of the lads in town and get some further footage. With great haste they started to make their way out.

"Try the pub on the corner first," the director yelled after crew, before turning to me. "Thanks, Darryl. You did well. We won't be needing you anymore today."

Marvellous! I was out of the door in a flash to visit some of my friends and to do some window shopping.

As I walked along the seafront, I felt sure that I saw two of the guests driving past me in a BMW. Much too fast, I can remember thinking as they jumped a red light. But I could have been mistaken. Well, I had a lovely afternoon out, and when I returned home I discovered three of the lads had already returned, but were busy popping in and out at intervals. I was impressed with how polite they were, and even loaned twenty pounds to one of them as he said he had lost his money in town and would repay me the next day.

Later that evening, when the minders had returned, the director caught up with them to reveal that one of the cameras had disappeared from the dining room. One of the crew went off with the director to search, first all the rooms and then the yard and back alley. Meanwhile, two of the lads returned, quietly trying to make their way upstairs, when the minder talking to me suddenly spotted them and shouted out for them to stop and come back down.

"Right you two, don't move! What's that you've just swallowed?" he asked one of them.

"Nothing guv, honest," came the reply, with the other one complaining bitterly at the same time about harassment.

"Alright," said the minder, "we can do this the easy way or the hard way. It's a strip search of you both here and now, or we can wait for my colleague to return and do a formal search with a police presence."

The lads agreed to the search now, to get it over with, and as I was about to leave the room, the minder turned to me and said, "If you don't mind, Darryl, I would like you to stay sitting at the back of the room to observe in the absence of my colleague. If I wait for him to come back, it will give these lads an opportunity to dispose of anything they might have on them."

"No problem," I said, with a gulp.

It was jolly interesting to see just what a detailed strip search actually involved. With both the lads standing facing the minder, he first got them to turn out their pockets and put all the contents on the dining room table. Thumbing through it, he found nothing untoward so he asked them to take off their shoes and then closely examined the insides of them and under the gap between the soles and the heels. Finding them okay, he dropped them on the floor behind him. Next, he carefully ran his hands through their hair, looked behind their ears, in their mouths and felt around their shirt collars and cuffs carefully before asking them to remove their belts and running his hands around the top banding of their jeans.

"Okay, strip and put all your clothing on the floor behind you," he told them, and without a murmur this is exactly what they did. It was as if they had been through this routine many times, and it seemed their only concern was they just wanted the minder to get on with it so they could go out again.

I could feel myself going quite red as I watched these two fit, well built young men with firm tight buttocks and washboard stomachs take off their shirts, then their jeans, followed by their underpants and finally their socks. They were altogether not unattractive.

The two lads, now stark naked in front of me, were each then subjected to the minder asking them to pull-up their scrotum and penis so that he could see if anything was attached or stuck out of sight. They then had to turn around and bend over whilst he closely looked in every crevice - interesting tattoos one of them had, quite rude - and finally they had to put their legs up behind them so that he could look at the soles of their feet and between their toes.

"Nothing this time," he said, "but I am watching the pair of you like a hawk. You can get dressed now and go. Oh, and thanks for your help, Darryl. Because of that we were able to get it over with quickly."

"No problem," I replied, "if you need me again, please don't hesitate to ask."

"Purvey bastard," one of the lads said over his shoulder, then added,"Probably a poof. Good job you were here, Darryl, or anything might have happened."

"Yes, yes, yes, I've heard it all before, same old record. Just get your clothes on and go or else you will return to the detention centre tonight," the minder told them casually.

With that, they quickly dressed and left.

Now, knowing that all of this would have been recorded on the cameras and would probably end up on the cutting room floor, I made it a mission to check the bins later that night and in the morning, just in case the tape or film had been thrown away. But no such luck. Blast! They never did find the missing camera either - just a few syringes behind the toilet at the top of the stairs. Good, I thought. Perhaps I would be asked to observe some more strip searches.

All seemed to go according to plan for the breakfasts, and every day I wandered about the town and left them to it as I had no rooms to do, no shopping, no cooking, and was even getting my lunch and dinner provided by the crew catering van. The only problem I had was that I received no post all week, but on Wednesday there was a delivery of parcels for one of the lads which he eagerly awaited in the hall, and again on Thursday and Friday. I had been sworn not to tell the minders. The lad told me it was sweets and clothes for all of them and if the officers found out, they would be confiscated.

On Thursday, Julian and Tristan came to tell me they had been broken into and their wide-screen TV had been removed from the wall and stolen, as had the video player and DVD player along with all their porn movies. Shame, because they said that they could claim for the equipment on their insurance but were unsure about the video collection.

Later that day, I had a visit from a huge guy who spoke with a deep south American accent and reminded me a bit of John Wayne. His diminutive wife was struggling to hang on to a large black dog that apparently was being trained to sniff for illegal rubbish dumping in the area. He introduced himself as being the neighbourhood watch boss for the area and told me he was investigating the break-in at Julian and Tristan's, saying he had followed a trail of video tape from their place to the area around my back alley and wanted to know if I had any knowledge of it.

Quite apart from this, it seemed there had been a number of car thefts in the past few days too. He promised, after gathering all the evidence he could find, to follow it up at the police station and get some answers as to who was responsible for bringing this crime-wave into his territory. They were a friendly couple, but he was quite insistent that he wanted to "Kick Arse" and get the area cleaned up.

Saturday, and needing some spending money, I went to the cash point only to discover I was up to my limit. After a few hasty phone calls to the card offices, I was informed that all the withdrawals had been on the new card sent to me last Monday. I told them that I had not had any post all week apart from the Parcel Force deliveries for my guests. By then, I was beginning to worry, and thought that I should bring it to the attention of the lads' minders. Something told me that all wasn't quite right.

Returning home, I found there was a police van outside and neighbours were watching from behind their windows, with Cynthia again polishing her railings as a policeman came out with one of the lads in handcuffs and put him in the back of the van. Pushing past the cameraman and other crew filming the whole affair, I entered the dining room to find the two minders angrily castigating the three lads there and questioning them as to the whereabouts of the other two. Of course, they either didn't know or were not saying anything, but a search of the rooms gave every indication they had done a runner. All that was left in the room shared by the two missing lads and the one in the back of the police van were three bunches of car keys for some expensive motors.

I informed the police officer there about my card problem, and my suspicions about not having any post other than parcel deliveries, which were in fact for those two missing lads.

"Well you have been a real pratt haven't you, Darryl?" the officer said. "You will need to make a statement down at the police station. The guardians of this little circle of misfits will probably be disciplined. It appears they have been spending every day down at the pub."

Later that night, the plain green mini-van that brought them all arrived to take the three remaining lads and the two minders back to the detention centre. What a disaster, I thought, and after all the expense and trouble by the film crew. But no, it wasn't. The director told me that it had been fantastic, even better than he could have hoped for! He assured me that with all the camera evidence of what was going on in the rooms coupled with the police work I should have no problem getting all my credit card money back, and he was excited about returning next year for the season. The pilot film, he claimed, was going to be a milestone in his career.

Thank God, it at last got around to Sunday and the film crew, after busily wrapping up all the equipment, departed, leaving only the fixed equipment and lighting remaining ready for the next seasons shoot in earnest. By the afternoon, after the local garage had brought some wheels for the catering van which had been found standing on bricks inb the morning, that too was removed.

All in all, it was not an un-eventful week!

August 5th

It was nice to have the place back to myself again. Naturally I missed having Lance around, but he had telephoned to say that he and his friend had moved into a bed-sit together and that he had managed to get a job as a driver's mate. He went on to tell me how much he missed being here with me and that he could not help thinking about the first night he had stayed and crept down to lie on my bed. He said he thought I was a nice sexy guy and how he had secretly wished I might have taken advantage of the situation that night.

That's typical, I thought, two lonely people fancying the pants of each other, and both afraid of offending, only to find out when it's too late. Never mind, there is always my profile on the Gaydar site, Darrylfromsouth. Nothing much from that yet, but you never know. Someone must come along one day!

The first job I had to tackle this week was the absence of a rear yard wall. There was no way I could leave it until the start of next season for when the film crew's catering van returned. I telephoned the director about it and he told me to get a local builder in to put up a temporary fence and send him the bill. That was no problem and I soon had Dave, my builder friend who initially did all the work for me, to get cracking on it. By Wednesday a six-foot fence and a gate was up at a cost of £387. I have paid David the money and sent a copy of the invoice to the film director, so now I feel safe again.

The unfortunate part of having the film crew here has been the trouble that the lads had got into. Instead of being a local celebrity for five minutes, with everyone wanting to know me, now I find there are hastily arranged meetings between the neighbours being made to discuss how to stop it happening again next season. The police are less than amused too, and the neighbourhood watch chief has suggested that if and when it all starts again, he should be informed so that a cordon can be arranged, with followers from his team of area coordinators shadowing my dubious residents wherever they go.

He has already produced a huge map and a spread sheet for what times and which area each of the coordinators will be covering. He is also going to contact the police to see if the lads can be tagged whilst here, and has arranged a meeting with the local council to see if he can get extra lighting in the surrounding streets with cameras set up on each corner. He does seem dedicated, even going so far as to schedule his diminutive wife to do a sandwich and flask round to all those on duty at the time.

The chairperson of the group business associations, Belinda, has invited me to a local meeting to explain myself. Having previously given her the impression it was to be a DIY television series, I am not looking forward to that at all. Already I have noticed that I've been dropped from the next garden party list in aid of the sand dune tree planting fund. During the week, I received letters from a number of local solicitors too, all of them seeking the address of the film company in order to pursue claims for damages for their clients, and a letter from the Home Office has requested me to give them a detailed account of the minders' activities.

The local paper has been running a story for the past

few days castigating the authorities for bringing a mini crime wave here, and I might add, they have not been complimentary about either me or my place. I've noticed too that Celia and Sonja, from the old people's home, have now started to put bicycle chains and locks around the wheelchairs whenever they wheel their residents outside to sit in the sun.

A visit from a council official Tuesday has worried me that there may be a planning issue. He wanted to know if I was envisaging a 'change of use', and has suggested that I might like to visit the planning department with plans of any building changes made. "Did I have a surveyor?" he asked. And blow me if the Fire Officer didn't call shortly afterwards to check the building. He was not a happy bunny, telling me that whilst I had the latest L2 system, he was not happy with the holes made in the walls for the girders and lighting cables, and insisting that I take no further guests in until this has been remedied and he has made a further visit. He wanted to know if I had done a new Fire Risk Assessment to reflect the changes that had been made.

John from the New Adventure Holiday Flats accompanied by the Chuckle Brothers have paid me a visit too. As some members of the new gay group have been questioning the possibility of me attracting gay bashers to S__, they suggested I might like to stand down from the committee. Reluctantly, I felt obliged to agree. They went on to say that the chairman, Gregory, elected only a couple of weeks ago, had with all the excitement of the evening suffered a minor stroke and passed the chair on to Patrick, who was keeping himself busy now with producing membership cards. He had bought a load of blank business cards and was, at that very moment, colouring them in by hand so that each member's name, written in copper plate script, would be appearing on a rainbow background. Should be posh, I thought.

Cynthia, 'all fur coat and no knickers' from next door, was horrified at what happened, but she did say that she had picked up a couple of new clients from the film company whilst talking to them over the back wall separating our yards. The creative director as well as the financial director could well turn out to be long-term visitors for her in the future. She and her husband invited me in for a drink and explained that, having got to know me over the past few months, they did not mind revealing to me they in fact ran a discreet gentlemen's guest house catering for their guests' more private needs.

After a couple of drinks, she got around to showing me her collection of nurses, police and other outfits, along with a selection of whips and canes that would have made Julian and Tristan envious. Naturally, this was all kept secret. They had run it this way ever since giving up a rented flat in Knightsbridge, when fortunately they had been able to buy the place outright. Most of her clients, she explained, were regulars of many years from London who were happy to make the journey here once a week. Explaining how, whilst she entertained her guests' needs, her husband would be in the wardrobe making video souvenirs for posterity, she added with a laugh that there was always a possibility they might later be needed for their retirement pension.

It turned out that what she and he husband were

bothered about was all the media and local interest caused by my film crew. Being only next door, this had made some of her guests nervous at the chance of being recognized. Amongst Cynthia's many clients there was a bishop, at least one MP, a chief of police, plus a plethora of others of equally high status. So, with this in mind, she suggested that if there was any way of me cancelling the next season's filming contract, she and her husband would be quite happy to help me financially for my loss of income. If I played my cards right, and was discreet, she said that they may be able to pass on any potential high-ranking gay clients to me who they were unable to accommodate themselves.

Could I get a cute but civilized up-market assistant to do the business with the guests for me, whilst I did the bit in the wardrobe, I wondered? At the very least Cynthia and her husband were willing to pay me for keeping my place low key, so it was definitely something to think about.

On Friday, I contacted the film company again as I wanted to check that they had received my invoice for the fence. I explained this over the phone, only to be told that any bills would go along with all the rest of the claims to the official receiver. Following many repercussions and litigations resulting from last week's shoot, the film company had announced yesterday that they were going into voluntary liquidation.

"What about my contract for next season?" I asked. "How about all the work I was promised to put my premises back to the way it was before they ripped it apart?"

"Well," the toffee-nosed tart at the other end said, "you

will have to bear in mind that the contract is not worth anything now. You will need to get all that work done yourself at your own expense and then submit all those costs to the receiver along with any writs or other claims that your solicitor might want to forward for loss of earnings. This may well take a few years of court proceedings because you will be on a long list of others in the same position, but do telephone me again if I can be of any further help, Darryl."

What a slapper! Help! She must be kidding!

Fortunately, I had already been paid for the rest of this season, and I do still have a lot of the company's lighting equipment and other stuff they left behind. That must be worth a few thousand quid, so they will definitely not be getting any of it back. I shall have to get David the builder to call around next week to give me a price for putting everything right. Maybe I can sell him the girders and some of the other stuff to help defray the cost, but in the meantime I will speak to Tristan and Julian to see if I can get a deal going with their friend who wanted to use my place to make a porn movie.

It seems that the only person not too bothered by all that happened last week was Raymond, a few doors away with the private parking and planted terrace. He said that he had put an old television and hi-fi out on his front ready to take to the tip, but someone had taken them along with the ten garden gnomes, bought for him by his friend Robin, whilst he was around the back getting his Rolls Royce out of the garage. He had assumed that it must have been one of my dubious guests, and about that he was quite pleased.

It was of little comfort at the time when Raymond told

me,

"Don't let it worry you, Darryl. You know how these things are, it will all be forgotten about in a few days. Just keep your head down."

Indeed, after a few gin and tonics downed whilst sitting out on his terrace, all seemed not so bad after all.

August 8th

Monday morning, and after contacting Dave to quote for the work needed to put my place back as it was before the film company got their hands on it, I asked Julian and Tristan to get some more information on their friend who made the porn movies. They told me they had been quite disappointed to learn their friend had given up the porn business because there were too many doing it live on websites and in chatrooms. He had since turned his hand to growing his own cannabis in a converted loft, and was currently looking for distributors. Always looking for new opportunities, Julian and Tristan revealed they were considering it themselves.

Business had been tough for them this year and they had considered trying to sell up, but having seen the numbers of guest houses and hotels on the market, and the drop in prices, they had decided to stick it out a little longer. To make ends meet, Julian had even thought about taking a job stacking shelves in the local supermarket. The meat counter, of course!

Letting their friend use my place to make porn films was now a non-starter, but it led me to think about the local art and technical college where they did all sorts of courses in film studies, both technical and visual. Without further ado, I contacted the principal and told him I was prepared to let out those rooms of mine which had all the lighting equipment and gantries for cameras still in place.

The students could use them at £50 per room per day. Much to my surprise, a lot of interest was shown, and on Tuesday a senior lecturer paid me a visit. He immediately booked the two bedrooms and the dining room. Over the next four weeks they will be used for various course projects, some on camera technique and others on making short films. It was a good result, and it will certainly help defray the builder's costs.

For the moment, I am enjoying the freedom of being able to check out the clubs and pubs, as I know within a month or two all the work will be completed and I shall be back to running my place again for guests. I have informed all the locals of the film company going bust, and of me reverting back to a normal business in the next two months. It seems to have calmed them down, including Belinda.

Tuesday, and it was off to a social with the new gay group. This time it was held at Dickeys Drive-In Hotel, which only had three parking spaces around the back of their place on a bit of waste ground next door, however they thought it added a touch of class and advertised it widely for the stag and hen groups, opening only for the weekends. It is a double-fronted property that is ever so slightly in need of renovation. All the windows in the place have been screwed shut to stop them falling out onto the street, and the chimney stacks lean at precarious angles.

When it rains, water cascades down from what is left of the guttering and the broken down-pipe on to the flat roof covering the bar/lounge. They call it their water feature. It is the only place I have seen with working gas wall-lights. They say they are handy for when the electricity goes off, and apparently that is fairly often, especially when they put on all the disco equipment at weekends. As they are only renting the place until it is pulled down, they cannot be doing with all the rules and regulations. Next door has already been demolished, leaving the side of their place shored-up with huge timbers, so they were going to make as much money as they could in the meantime.

The guys that run the place, Norman and Fred, own two Dobermans and claim they have very little trouble from guests. They do seem butch enough to look after themselves. They had made their bar/lounge look homely. I noticed the decorated huge Chinese urns that were strategically placed under the areas with missing and stained ceiling tiles, and was laughingly told they were 'a bit of a bugger to empty after a good old downpour.' There was a large flat-screen television on one wall, and the bar occupied the whole of another, whilst the third wall catered for the DJ console and the glitter balls. All the walls seemed to have been decorated in left-over rolls of wallpaper, as every few strips became a different pattern and colour.

With the bar/lounge also serving as the dining room, all the tables had been pushed in front of the double window that fronted the street so that with the drawn, heavy, black, moth-eaten curtains, they made an effective stage area for the karaoke that came later.

Norman and Fred had gone to a lot of trouble to provide a buffet. Along half of the bar they had set out sandwiches of salmon, ham, cheese and egg next to pork pies, quiches, gateauxs and a good mix of salads. They had prepared it all the previous day and, having covered it in rather grubby and slightly damp tea towels, they had thoughtfully left a table fan blowing over it at full speed, even leaving it on all night, to keep any flies away.

Without any neighbours, they could have the disco as loud as it would go. Invariably, it was at a level that distorted the sound and, whenever an announcement was made through the microphone, the high-pitched whistle that ensued had everyone clasping their ears until hasty adjustments were made to the console. The well-scratched and cigarette burnt laminate floor shook with every step one took across it, and when someone accidentally dropped a pen, we all watched, fascinated, as it rolled away to a corner of the room.

Some of the group complained about the bar prices being a tad high, dearer even than the clubs, but in fairness, Norman quickly turned the tariff board around to display a much cheaper menu. "Sorry," he said, "I meant to do that earlier. Still, never mind, what's a few pence matter to me? We need to finish off this barrel anyway."

Eventually, the buffet was declared open and it was a chance to make the announcements for the new group, which incidentally has changed its name from SOS to "S__ Hotel Area Gay" - SHAG for short. Patrick, our new leader and chairman, had already produced leaflets and a SHAG logo in big, bold, gold lettering to go up on the new web-site that Danny and Sidney, the Chuckle Brothers, were putting together.

They in turn had been working on listing all the members' establishments, and adding pictures of them along with short descriptions of what was available to any potential visitors. The banner, in brightly coloured large letters that moved across the top of page, read,

Wanting A Shag Place To Stay in S__?

Look No Further!

Someone suggested putting links on the site to sell underwear and magazines, saying perhaps it should even have a chat room. Norman thought it would be a good idea if his phone number was put on the home page as he and Fred would be more than willing to man the telephone twenty-four hours a day. They could take deposits on their PDQ machine and pass on the bookings to individual members, provided they told them what availability they had a few days in advance. He would then deduct a small amount from the deposits to cover his costs, prior to forwarding the balances at the end of each month.

Danny and Sidney were quick to point out that this would not work. I think they were a bit suspicious of Norman's motives, but too polite to say so. Danny said that if they did anything like that, it would have to be fully automated through a booking agency, where obviously there would be a small charge, but the group funds would also get a small commission.

Dave, from the Dandelion Hotel, was concerned that any members who were not online all the time would lose out to those that were - they would be creating a two-tier group which favoured the clever arses with computers - but Patrick stated it was up to the members to have a proper system in place. If they didn't, then that was their problem. They were supposed to be running professional businesses, so there could be no room for the complacent in the organization.

"Hang on," shouted Tracy from the Sun Kissed Villa, "we thought this was supposed to be a social group where we helped each other. It looks more like some are trying to cream off the business for themselves."

"Well," replied Patrick, "we do have to move with the times. I am already looking to form a buying group for the members, and some of my suppliers are interested. Members could telephone me with their orders for jams, butters, loo rolls and anything else, and I would take delivery of them, then later they could collect their order from me. I can buy slightly cheaper in bulk and pass on some of the savings to the members. I could also do something similar by advertising all members under the SHAG banner in gay magazines."

At this point everyone wanted to talk at once, and some quite heatedly, until Raymond interjected and suggested that the committee should hold another meeting to discuss all the proposals in detail. So, with a sigh of relief from everyone, it was back to the warm beer and the raffle where I managed to win a box of out-of-date butters, kindly donated by Norman. The proceeds, a healthy £45 in an old shoe box, was quickly claimed by Patrick who passed it on to John, the treasurer, for the group funds, but it was quickly wrestled back by Norman to pay for the buffet. Yet another heated debate ensued. This one about who would pay for the sandwiches.

People started putting them back on to the bar, even with teeth marks in them, and furtively tried to back away, but once again Raymond came to the rescue suggesting that the money be split on this occasion between SHAGs and Dickeys Drive-In Hotel. Norman agreed, and his partner was instructed to put the Dobermans away again.

The rest of the evening was entertaining, with the

karaoke and a few lewd jokes from our hosts. At around eleven, a steady drip, drip, drip into the Chinese urns told us that it had started to rain, and soon afterwards wisps of smoke could be seen coming from three multi-plug adapters in a four way extension lead that supplied power to the disco lighting. Fred rushed to pull some of them out, and the sudden gloom provided people with a good opportunity to start leaving.

Soon we were all on our way home. Fortunately, Raymond had arrived in his old Rolls Royce with his friend Robin, so along with Celia and Sonja, who had wrapped the left-over buffet in newspapers and taken it because it was "a shame to see it go to waste when it will treat residents tomorrow afternoon sitting outside in their wheelchairs", I climbed into the Roller for a grand ride home in style. At the last moment, Andrew and Kelly managed to squeeze in too and sat down on a pile of sandwiches which immediately spewed mayonnaise onto the back seat.

"Sorry, Raymond. They are pressed beef now," one of them quipped. "Damn," Celia exclaimed, "they were the salmon ones I was going to have for breakfast."

On the way home, Andrew and Kelly from the Pastel Hotel, who were also on the SHAG committee, started to question where the new group was going. It appeared to be running away from being just a social group, they claimed. They said that Patrick and the new couple from Dickeys Drive-In only seemed to be interested in what was in it for themselves, and earlier they had overheard the three of them discussing divvying up any enquiries that might come through the new website.

"Over my dead body," said Celia. "I shall write a strong letter of complaint to the secretary of SHAGs."

"You are the secretary," Kelly reminded her.

Always a stickler for correct procedure, Celia responded,

"It still has to go through the proper channels. I can't possibly put it on the agenda for the next committee meeting if I don't have a formal written complaint."

Sonja, her partner who had said little all evening and seemed quite content sipping on a glass or two of rather cheap red wine, suddenly interjected with,

"Is it true that the place where all the rent boys go - you know, the one that does the lap dancing and has the male strippers in cages - are also members of the group?"

"Don't be silly," said Andrew, "that would bring us into disrepute. We would look like a bunch of sleaze-bags with knocking shops. Respectability is why Julian and Tristan haven't been asked to join."

"As it happens," Celia replied, "they are members. Patrick signed them up along with Norman and Fred. They all like the club, and Patrick can be seen there occasionally, on his knees with his tongue out in front of the cages, more in hope than expectation, I imagine."

"It looks like we will have a lot to discuss at the next meeting," said Raymond, a master of the understatement.

As I arrived home, it crossed my mind that perhaps it was a good thing I had been asked to stand down from the committee. Running the group looked difficult, and was best left to the experts. Still, the socials looked to be fun, and I hope they keep them going. They make a change from the same old pubs and clubs. You can talk to the other members and get to know them.

September 3rd

Three more weeks and the season is well and truly finished. Everyone seems to agree what a terrible year it has been. Already, when walking along the prom, there is little apparent tourist activity, with only the occasional couple of pensioners to be seen huddled together in the shelters away from the cold breeze, some sharing sandwiches and a flask of tea as they wait for the Bingo Hall to open or the show on the end of the pier to start. Unlike up North in Blackpool, the guest houses and hotels here are already beginning to close for the winter.

Perhaps I should have moved to Blackpool after all. At least there they manage to go on until November, and even right through the year for those in the area around the North Shore. With the huge Pleasure Beach, all the pubs and clubs, the lights and the many shows, it must be fabulous to get away for Christmas, so I might try to take a break there myself for the New Year. As I will probably need to book well in advance, I shall check out a couple of the websites later. That will give me something to do tonight.

Never mind, there is at least some light on the horizon for me. My gorgeous friend with the lovely tight black trousers, Colin, from the mortuary where I worked before changing career, has telephoned to ask if I would be interested in hosting their annual staff outing and prize-giving do. It is always taken at the beginning of November, prior to the funeral trade's busiest period which is over the winter months, with loads of overtime at Christmas. Of course, I was interested and eagerly agreed to do it.

They have booked for fifteen of them to arrive on the Friday night and stay until Sunday morning, with another ten coming on the Saturday just for the presentations and pep talk by the Funeral Director. This usually lasts for about an hour-and-a-half and consists of trying to get the front of house staff to sell the more expensive coffins and silk linings.

It used to be a big competition to see who could sell the biggest marble headstones too, but the bottom of this market has dropped out since all the cemeteries started to landscape, so now it is about promoting other extras like pendants for ashes that relatives can wear, and bronze cremation urns. There will also be prizes for the mortuary staff for how much they have saved on equipment, things such as bone-cutting forceps and rib-cutting shears, injection and aspiration equipment, and head block rests which were often taken home by the staff to jack-up their cars when working underneath them.

I have been asked to set out a couple of tables in the dining room for one of their biggest suppliers to give a presentation and provide samples of their embalming fluids, and arterial fluids along with the latest make-up products which are always of interest to Andrew and Tom who do the final presentation of the corpses and press them down into the coffins.

Excellent! It will be a nice little earner for me, plus I will have a chance to join in the party afterwards with all my old friends.

Other than this good news, it has been a boring week, and even were I to be open, the telephone has been eerily silent. Whilst in town shopping, I did happen to bump into

Norman and Fred who held the SHAG social last week. We had a cup of tea from the roadside chip van that parks opposite the cottages in the ornamental gardens. This is one of their favourite places as they are able to watch the talent coming and going whilst the Dobermans have a run around. Generally discussing the poor season, they gave me the benefit of their knowledge on cost-cutting during these lean times. They had decided to remove all the kettles from their bedrooms to save on providing hospitality trays, taken away the ironing and hair-drying facilities - these were now charged for as an extra - and for breakfast they would now give just one slice of toast, if asked for! They revealed that they usually managed to get a lot of free food from their nightly trip to the skips at the back of the supermarket, and were pleased that the majority of the SHAG's buffet had come this way.

Apparently, we were supposed to have had chicken drumsticks as well that night but whilst they were laid out all along one end of the bar, the Dobermans got to them first. They told me they also did well for boxes of cracked eggs from the skip. If they were bad, they were put to one side and, after complaining to the egg man when he came with the next delivery, he would swap them for a new tray.

The bar provided them with even more opportunities to save money. They would change the labels on the cheap spirits bought at the corner shop, or on one their frequent trips across the channel for fags and booze, with brand leaders' labels steamed from bottles gathered from the bottle bank at the council tip. As well as this, once three-quarters of it had been sold, they often moaned at the brewery telling them the last barrel of lager was off and would get a credit note for another one.

They have even managed to get free gas and electricity. With the property next door to them having been demolished, somehow they had managed to locate the electricity supply line to it which went along the bottom of their cellar wall. Wearing several pairs of rubber gloves, and with Wellington boots on their feet whilst using a large insulated hammer, they managed to drive six-inch nails into both the positive and negative cables. With great care, and some giant bulldog clips, they had been able to attach cables to run the supply into their own fuse box.

The gas, they said, was a lot easier. All they had to do was turn the gas off and then, with a large spanner, undo the nuts on both sides of the meter and turn it around to face the wall, before doing the nuts up again and turning the gas back on. This made the meter run backwards. However, after two months it needed to be turned back again and watched carefully to ensure (a) too much wasn't used and (b) enough was actually shown on the dials to take it just over the last reading. The last thing they wanted was for the supplier to discover that the reading was less than before, so sometimes this necessitated putting the heating, the gas rings, grill and oven on at full blast for a day or two, which at least cured the damp for a while.

Never ones to miss a trick, they had also managed to reduce their water charges by connecting to the old supply for next door and running a pipe up to their tank in the loft, however their laundry charges had at first been much more difficult to cut costs on. Nevertheless, with a little planning they had found a way. With three baskets purloined from the hospital some months earlier and now kept at the back of their hotel, they would arrive at the local hospital prior to the hospital's laundry service vehicle at six in the morning and put them amongst the pile of dirty laundry baskets.

Once the driver had exchanged the dirty baskets for the same number containing freshly pressed, clean laundry and left, they would quickly take three away with them. This did not always go entirely to plan as occasionally they would return to the hotel to find that one of the baskets contained theatre gowns, or an assortment of pyjamas and smocks. In spite of this, they had managed to reduce their laundry costs dramatically, and all the sheets were beautifully starched.

Quite often, the two rogues got bookings for the stag and hen weekends courtesy of the hotel opposite. When Norman bought his new laptop, he discovered that being wire free - WiFi, I think he called it - he could read the other hotel's emails and would then telephone some of their enquirers himself. Apparently, unlike him, the twats over the road had no fire wall installed. Under the circumstances, with Norman and Fred having no working fire alarm, just an old panel that blinked in the hall, I imagined that fire wall would at least be of some help to them.

Declaring to the authorities that only Norman worked the hotel, Fred was able to claim unemployment benefit and a rent and rates allowance. They were also in the process of claiming invalidity benefit for a back injury which occurred, they said, when Fred saved an old age pensioner in a wheelchair from being crushed by a falling tree by holding it up until she was dragged clear. Naturally, there were no witnesses, but after several visits to the doctor and a specialist, it was all going to plan. Norman felt there might even be some mileage in him claiming for a carer's allowance as well.

I asked them if running the Rover was expensive, and was told that with the number plates copied from Fred's doctor's car fixed to theirs, they did not have to bother with tax, insurance, or as it happens with any speeding or parking fines. They managed to fill it up every week with fuel from the guests' cars parked on the waste ground at the back of their place. Easy, they said, and explained. Insisting vehicle keys are left at reception on arrival for health and safety reasons, once the guests go out for the evening, Norman takes a length of hose and a five gallon drum and siphons the petrol from their cars, leaving just enough for them to get a few miles down the road before running out. They had even managed to get a nearly new set of tyres from a guest's car for the Rover.

These were not the sort of people I wanted to associate with, I began thinking, in spite of them buying the tea, and I was pleased for this respite on the bench to come to an end when they announced it was time for their daily jog with the Dobermans around the gardens.

Oh well, next week I shall at least be a busier with the students coming to do their projects, and it is only from nine to four with no meals or overnight stays. It should be a doddle as they can have their tea breaks at the café on the corner. The lecturers are the only ones who will have keys, so there are no worries about security.

Dave has given me a price and date for completing the work at my place. It all looks to be on schedule, and he can work around the students filming in some of the rooms. He hopes to have it all done by the middle of November, so as nothing much will be happening in S__ between then and Easter, it looks like Blackpool, here I come for Christmas!

September 12th

At 8.30 Monday morning, I was rushing around to ensure the three bedrooms and the dining room were ready for the lecturers and students from the local college when they arrive. There was nothing much else I could do as I didn't know what it was exactly that they wanted.

The first lecturer arrived at 9.45 and was not a bit like the earlier film director. This one was a bearded, dour man in his tweed coat, the type of coat with leather patches on the elbows which, when he took it off, revealed his cardigan had similar patches, and he constantly mumbled to himself in between telling me that the other three lecturers would be following on at midday along with all the students and equipment.

He was a bit of a pain and wanted to know if I had flip charts, dry wipe boards, paper, pencils and erasers etc. I told him I had none of those things and off he shot back to his college to return later with all the above and what seemed like mountains of books and manuals. Still mumbling and tutting to himself, and constantly moving a table or chair first this way then that way, he spent an hour carefully laying out notebooks and pencils on every table in the dining room until it began to look like a lecture theatre.

Later, he asked me to get rid of all the furniture in the three bedrooms, but to still have some items available should they require them, so that kept me busy until the rest of the students and lecturers arrived. I heaved and struggled to get all this kit into the adjoining rooms from where, if they needed any of it, they could get it themselves, and decided there and then that was enough, I wasn't going to be their porter for the duration.

Whilst they were together in the dining room, now a lecture theatre, I hovered around outside the door listening to the schedule they were planning for the next four weeks. The students were being split into three groups and given a project, each very different. This first week was to be mostly classroom based on the theory of what they were undertaking (Oops, been there before!) with the second and third weeks used for the projects assigned to them, leaving the fourth week for reviewing the work achieved.

One group were to make a short kitchen sink drama, a second group a horror film and the third a documentary on conflicts in the African sub-continent during the 1890s. How they handle the latter project, made in a bedroom upstairs, should prove interesting!

The senior lecturer told me to ignore them all, which suited me fine, and everything went well this first week. They came and went, sometimes to be seen carrying African head dresses, stuffed animals, costumes or even a couple of old tailor's dummies with knives poking out of their chests which sported great splodges of blood-red paint. Cynthia, next door, was relieved the youngsters seemed to be a better class of student than she usually came across in town.

She didn't mind them a bit, especially as they all went home in the late afternoon and left the house empty until the following morning. The occasional scream or banging of tom-toms from the rooms upstairs never lasted for too long.

Wednesday evening saw Julian and Tristan paying me

a visit, just to be nosey. They were fascinated to see all the props and costumes in the bedrooms and, with my permission, rushed back home only to return straightaway with a digital camera so they could take turns in dressing up and photographing each other. At one stage, Julian found the black greasepaint and after stripping promptly covered himself in it. He then put on a grass skirt, a huge black fuzzy wig and a rubber bone with protrusions to hold it in place in his nostrils. These, with a necklace of imitation tiger teeth around his neck whilst holding a spear, made him look very much the part, especially with his portly frame, and he could not resist swinging his hips back and forth to allow his pink manhood to peek through the grass skirt.

It was not long before Tristan stripped and adorned the white hunter's costume. The pair then had me photographing them in all sorts of poses, some a bit risqué I might add. I suggested to them that what they were doing was probably not how the first meeting between a white hunter and an African king had gone, but on second thoughts, perhaps it did! This carried on for some time, and indeed it was great fun, but with all of us laughing so much, I was worried Cynthia next door might hear.

Julian wanted to wear his African outfit as long as possible, and he did make a dramatic, if slightly camp spectacle sitting on the settee in my lounge with a gin and tonic in a plastic monkey's skull in one hand and the spear in the other. His legs, the varicose veins hardly visible through the grease paint, stretched out in front of him to reveal everything he had through the grass skirt. It was soon after this that he went upstairs to use the loo, still clutching his spear. A sudden scream, followed by a loud thump as his frame hit the floor, had Tristan and I rushing upstairs to see what had happened.

We found Julian passed out cold, but fortunately he appeared not to be injured. He soon came round, with the help of Tristan rubbing him in all sorts of areas to get his blood circulating again. It was an unusual revival technique, one I could not recall ever watching on any of those hospital programs, but hey ho, it seemed to work.

It turned out that Julian, on opening the loo door and reaching in to put the light on, had caught sight of one of the tailor's dummies sitting on the pan, with knives sticking out of its chest. Another one was hanging by its collar from the coat hook on the back of the door. The students had left them there, out of the way. Silly me, I should have warned him.

Never mind, he recovered and I then left them alone whilst they took off the costumes and spent an eternity in the shower together washing all the greasepaint off, or so I believed that was what they were doing. We did have a great evening, and in spite of them being absolute trollops, I can't help liking them. It was gone midnight before they eventually left, much the worse for wear.

Seeing the way the dining room had been set up to resemble a lecture theatre earlier in the week, and the way in which the group had organized themselves, gave me an idea of how I might improve my turnover next season. It needed to improve, especially as I had not taken many guests in, certainly not enough to build up a repeat customer base. I thought, what if I ran a course for potential hoteliers? Those people looking to buy hotels and guest houses who were coming into the business for the first time knowing absolutely nothing, much as I had done. I could advertise and run my own course over, say, three or four days at £150 per couple per day, including accommodation and evening meals.

This led me to plan a course based on four couples at a time. That would be £1,800 minimum - nice! They would be split into four teams on arrival, and after an introductory talk and being shown their rooms along with the location of everything else in the place, I would take them all out for a fish and chip supper and a drink in one of the quieter pubs to do the 'Get to know each other stuff'. The next morning, Team A would have to be up early to receive hands on training in preparing and serving breakfast, also learning how to clear down the kitchen, make up the rooms, vacuum and polish throughout, go to the shops to buy food for lunches, then after cooking a light lunch and clearing down again, how to start preparing the evening meal.

Team B on their first day would have the task of dealing with minor maintenance issues like keeping the outside areas swept and clean, putting the laundry through the washing machine and dryers and doing the pressing whilst at the same time dealing with arrivals and departures with the other two teams role-playing as difficult guests. There was always the possibility of actually getting real guests in to give them a realistic experience, especially as it will be them doing all the work for me. I would need to have an advertising campaign running to try and fill the place during the courses. For all the extra services that could be provided with such a plethora of staff, I should be able to charge the genuine guests a few pounds more per night.

Teams C and D would spend their first day in the classroom having talks on how to assess a property to buy, how to build relationships with accountants, solicitors, environmental health and planning departments, and the fire service. I could give them an exercise to do every hour or so, whilst I chased up and advised the other teams on the order and procedure of what they needed to accomplish. The afternoon would be based on how to manage accounts and advertising, followed by the legal requirements for health and safety. I could even get a nice glossy handbook printed for them to keep. That would be good, I thought, wondering if I could charge separately for it!

On the second day Teams A and B would swap with teams C and D, so by the third day they should all have a good idea of what is involved, and the amount of work needed, in running a guest house or hotel, so on that third and last full day they could all muck-in together and decide amongst themselves who would do what task. I will call this the Management and Leadership Skills Day.

On the fourth day, all they would have to do, after packing their luggage, would be to put into practice one last time getting the place ready for letting. Maybe I could produce a pretty certificate on the computer for them to take home, and perhaps for another five pounds put it in a gold-edged frame bought from Woolworth. I needed to work on how to spin it out though, if I was going to make it last over four days. Perhaps I should include running a bar. I don't have one myself, so I would have to research this first. Do you buy the license at the post office, or what? It can't be that difficult pulling a pint and slapping a bag of crisps down on the counter, can it?

I might consider asking Julian and Tristan to cover this bit for me, after all they do have a bar, but we would have to forget using the harp to slice the lemons - it would be much too heavy to carry up the road.

September 30th

Another week has shot by. Dave, with his small team of decorators, are steaming ahead and making good progress putting the place to rights, in between dodging the students working on their projects in the three bedrooms.

On Tuesday I had a visit from a county-wide tourist association. They want to include me on their web-search pages for guest houses and hotels in the area. At only £25 for the first year, it seems worth a try. The woman left me a questionnaire to fill in so I could describe my property, the idea being that people looking for accommodation could put in their exact requirements and the establishments that best match them will be listed first. The questions were easy to answer, just a series of check boxes, although some were a bit vague as to the interpretation.

- Do you have en-suites? Well, I do have some so I ticked yes.
- Do you have car parking? I don't have any personally, but there are car parks only two streets away, so I had to tick yes to this as well.
- Do you have internet access? Only on my own computer in the bedroom, so strictly I do, therefore this also had to be a yes.
- Do you provide evening meals? I could run down to the fish and chip shop if I wanted a booking, so it was yes to this.
- Do you have a bar? I had to say yes to this too, although it's not available to guests. Being at

the bottom of my kitchen cupboard it's there in case any friends drop round.

- Do you have facilities for children? This was a bit tricky, but if I bought one of those plastic blow-up paddling pools, I could get it out of the box and put in the yard should anyone ever ask for facilities, and there are plenty of books around to put on a dining room chair to make the seat higher, so it was a yes to this one also.
- Tick your main customer base it asked, providing selections for older people, younger people, children, gay, gay friendly, straight, mixed and so on. It was a yes to all these too! Just a no to the stag and hen parties.
- Are you close to public transport? An easy one. It's only a short walk to the bus stop and station, twenty minutes, if you're fit, would cover it fine, so another yes.

By the time I came to the end of the questionnaire, there were eighty-three ticks for yes and two for no. I think this should put me first on any search someone might do on their site. Completed, I bunged it into the post-box. They even provided a free stamped envelope.

The students continued to come and go, doing their own thing. Dave agreed that if I wanted to go away for a few days, he would look after them for me by locking up once they left in the afternoons and opening up the following morning. He was around all day and knew the property and all about the alarm system, so a quick amendment to the Fire Risk Assessment to include him left me free to visit some acquaintances in Scotland for a few days.

Dave and Doug retired into a huge old mobile home some years ago, one they had cleverly disguised as a bungalow by digging trenches into which to sink the wheels. In earlier days they had run their own hotel in Glasgow where all the guests were expected to make up their own rooms and cook their own breakfasts. Apparently they were successful, eventually selling it in order to breed camels in the highlands.

Their thinking was that, apart from the meat, they could also sell the camel hair to the rag trade to make coats, and the hides to shoe manufacturers. At one point they had over thirty of the beasts in a huge barn. They were mostly imported from Mongolia and Russia so were well at home in the lower temperatures of Scotland.

This turned out to be a short lived venture. The meat content in older camels tends to be tough and not very tasty, and in younger camels it is a bit like course beef. The cut of meat also determines its tenderness, with the hump being considered a delicacy. That is eaten raw whilst still warm, but after it cools down it is boiled before being eaten. However, despite many weeks of attempting to get the butchers and restaurants to purchase any volume, the results were poor. The camel riding lessons had also attracted little response.

Breeding also became a particular nightmare for them as the courting and mating can be extremely violent. If the male selects a female and she is not willing to go down quietly when he approaches her, he will bite at her neck and roughly force her to the ground. The female utters her guttural protest while the male first straddles her and then gently slides down until he is squatting on his back legs. Copulation lasts for about fifteen minutes and is accompanied by much gurgling and grunting. The male is normally docile and easily controlled. However, in the rutting season, he can become so aggressive that he is dangerous and cannot be handled. Not dissimilar to our own species! He is extremely restless and his lips are often covered with saliva. The glands between the ears secrete a dark, bad-smelling, watery secretion. This area is constantly rubbed against all objects in the surroundings, including grass mounds. The back legs are spread and the tail is then beaten against the penis. Drops of urine are deposited on the tail and spread over the back until eventually the hindquarters have a strong urine odour.

Rutting males readily attack each other, so timid males soon learn to keep away from the territory staked out by more aggressive males. Now this was a particular problem for Dave and Doug, especially at nights when trying to round them up to get them into the barn for their meal of chopped hay and straw. So, after finding them homes in various zoos around the country and filling their freezers to maximum with the best cuts of meat, they abandoned the venture in favour of breeding pedigree cats, eventually selling up, yet again, on their retirement. Now they exist solely by buying the odd car and selling it on eBay, after Doug has rewired it - a bit of a fetish he has always had.

It was a change to get away from S__ for a few days, especially as it is now so quiet. One of the effects of living such a boring, solitary existence where nothing much happens is that I have decided, at least for the time being, to write my diary less frequently. I hope this decision isn't too distressing for my number one fan, a lighting engineer in one of the most famous theatres in the country, and someone of whom I have the greatest respect. Given the height of the theatre, and the many light bulbs that obviously need constantly changing, his steps must be absolutely huge!

October 14th

Staying with my old friends in their dotage up in Scotland had been a real break, quietly enjoying sitting all day in the hazy sunshine, wearing our thermal underwear and overcoats, watching the many cats playing around the fish pond, occasionally dipping and swiping a paw into the water attempting to catch one of the coy carp, but all too soon it was time to get back to S__ again, though not before spending a little more time in Blackpool where it was my intention to book a few nights away for the New Year festivities.

A couple of hours on the train with an easy change at Preston, and I was arriving at Blackpool North Station, right in the heart of the gay area. Being a Wednesday, especially at this time of year, I was surprised at how busy it was. Walking along the road from the station, I discovered most of the guest houses were actually showing *No Vacancy* signs in their windows.

I did consider trying the guest house I'd stayed at earlier in the year with all my friends when we came up for the Blackpool Pride, but decided against it. The owner, the chap with the one leg, tended to wake you up early in the morning clunking up and down stairs changing the loo rolls and towels.

Around the first corner I spotted a vacancy sign and there appeared to be life within and without. Two legs were poking out from underneath the back of a car and an old rusty and pitted exhaust pipe was propped up by the garden wall. Tapping gently on the car boot lid, I politely enquired if the owner was around.

"Yes, that's me. What can I do for you?" came a voice from under the car, without any attempt from its owner to see who I was.

"Do you have a single room for one night, maybe two?" I asked.

"Don't do maybes," he said, "or one-nights. If it's for two nights then that I can do. The rooms are all standard and well appointed with everything you might need. I do a good cooked breakfast and run a quiet establishment," he said, sliding a box of spanners from under the car and kicking them clear of his feet. At £17 a night it seemed ridiculously cheap, and two nights would give me the option of staying longer if I wanted to, so I said, "Yes please, I would like to book for two nights, if that is alright."

"Right," he said, "give me a second, I'll come out and let you look at the room first. If you like it, we can book you in and settle up. Sorry about this, but I had to put on a new exhaust pipe. It's just about finished, at last."

With that, there was a lot of struggling and wriggling as the man tried, his legs flailing about in vain, to get out from under the car.

"Bugger, bugger, bugger! I've bolted up the new one and can't get out. Would you mind gently giving a few pumps on that bottle jack to raise the car a bit?"

No problem. A few pumps lifted the car clear of his slight paunch and out he struggled, covered in oil and mud.

"Thank you very much," he said. "You seem a decent enough young man. Go in and up the stairs to Room One. If it's alright for you, make yourself comfortable. You can come down and settle up a bit later when I've cleaned myself up a bit. Let me know if there is anything that you need."

How strange, I thought to myself, this man is so much like Raymond in S__, perhaps a bit younger but with the same sort of directness and affability, although with all that oil and dirt over his face he could have been any age.

The room was indeed comfortable, and bigger than I would have expected. It had central heating, television, hot water, decent clean carpeting, plus another wall-mounted radiant heater, and not a payment meter in sight. The bed was comfortable and the loo was right next door, but no shower room was evident as I went downstairs after settling in. Perhaps there wasn't one, but that didn't matter. For two nights I could strip-wash at the sink in my room.

I gave a polite cough as I approached the owner's private door, which was open. I could hear him in there talking with someone.

"Come on in," he called out. "We're all friends here."

So in I went, not knowing exactly what to expect. Sitting on the settee, talking to the landlord, was the elegant man who had offered to take my photograph on the pier earlier in the year before he dashed off to the green room to photograph the stars. What's more, he instantly recognised me.

"Hello again," he said. "I remember you. You and your friends were here for the Pride Weekend, weren't you. Those lovely tight black trousers you were wearing have been etched in my memory ever since. Have you brought your friends with you again this time?"

"Not this time," I replied. "I'm here on my own for a couple of nights, and to book a room for the New Year."

The landlord, named Pedro, after getting me to sign-in and swiftly taking my payment, introduced me to Wayne. The guy was not looking quite so elegant this time. There were beads of perspiration on his forehead and his shoes had been kicked off. He explained that he had just returned from giving tap dancing lessons in the Tower Ballroom to one of the many Derby and Joan clubs that came by the coach load to see the Blackpool Illuminations. It was something he did most days, simply to get himself out of the house.

His main source of income came from royalties on the books he had written. Currently he was working on another one, something about disturbances of retinoid activated transcription mechanisms being implicated as risk factors for schizophrenia, a sequel to his last book, The Guinea Pig's Games Room. As if this was not enough, he apparently had his own website too, dedicated to commenting on news from both the gay and the straight world. Phew!

Pedro offered and made me a cup of coffee before refreshing his and Wayne's vodka and coke that I was looking at enviously. Wayne proceeded to enquire, once I was comfortably seated in an armchair, where was I from, what did I do for a living, was I single, how old I was, where had I worked, did I have a car, what hobbies I had and what was I doing in the future? You know, the sort of questions that one occasionally interjects slowly in a conversation. Much better, I conceded, to get them all out of the way in one go. As it happens, we all got on like a house on fire, especially once they knew I was in the hospitality trade, too. So much so that Pedro telephoned a guest house nearby to request some more gin, apparently stored there. This was some sort of private gentleman's club consisting of the two members. By now, I was feeling slightly guilty that the purpose of my trip was to look for accommodation over the New Year, but I was honest with Pedro, hoping that he would not be miffed by my not asking to book there. With so many of the establishments having great bars, and some clubs even having accommodation attached to them, it seemed to be a better idea to book in at one of these. After all, if I got lucky at the more raunchy ones, it would merely be a few steps to my room, without having to sneak someone in. Fabulous! I could probably spend all my time there, without ever having to leave. There was bound to be some with fancy dress, or even no dress at all, in the posher ones, and with no worries about having to traipse through the streets to get to a club. I quite fancied an underwear party, to sleep all day and party all night.

Pedro was not the slightest bit bothered and was even tremendously helpful in suggesting which establishments did what. He even gave me a list that I could take home of all the gay places in the local gay accommodation group. Even so, I decided that I would be better to look on line, there being so many websites listed. Clearly, the best were going to be those attached to the gay venues with their own accommodation, and these would fill up first.

I gave thanks that our group in S__ didn't allow anything but privately owned hotels, otherwise those of us with the small guest houses would not have had a chance. If we were to allow companies like that in, they might soon be thinking of making taking over the entire group, even to the point of inveigling their way into our committee. With their bigger and bolder offerings, they might exclusively attract the gay trade to themselves. I could see that Blackpool with its tremendous gay life could encompass this, but in S__ we were still trying to appeal to a cross-section of customers. We were wary of letting any members of the group suggest anything but a reasonable propriety that would appeal to all.

Wayne suggested that, if I was stuck, he wouldn't mind putting me up free of charge. Such a nice guy! I almost considered it until he gave me the impression his home was a sort of miniature Blackpool Zoo and a lot of his time had to be dedicated to looking after his animals. However, I was more than keen to suggest that we all had a meal out together over the festive season.

All the time we were talking, the telephone was constantly ringing with Pedro either taking bookings or refusing them, and I wondered, what was so special about this place that, in spite of it having no en-suites or bar, it was in such demand. Pedro was constantly muttering to himself about overbooking and always writing stuff down, as if it was too much to remember.

The afternoon flew by, coming to an end when Wayne said he had to leave whilst he could still stand. Collecting his heavy carrier bags of pet food and straw, he stumbled off, promising we would all meet again. Thanking Pedro profusely for his hospitality, I left before his gin-supplier friend arrived for another tipple.

That evening, I took the opportunity to stroll the miles of illuminations along Blackpool's promenade. What a truly magnificent spectacle! It is no wonder the season is that much longer here than anywhere else in the country. There are fortunes to be made running a hotel in Blackpool.

A few drinks in the local bars, all fairly quiet being mid-week, was a nice way to round off the day. Unlike abroad, where one is often accosted by locals with armfulls of wristwatches, or necks festooned with dozens of supposedly gold and silver necklaces, in Blackpool, especially after dark, it's the drug peddlers who find you, brazenly offering speed, coke, uppers, downers or whatever your fix happens to be, and they can be equally difficult to get rid of.

The next morning, having made up my mind to stay another night, I decided to look along the road where all the bigger gay guest houses seemed to be. Breakfast was taken in a bright, airy bay windowed room, myself and three other elderly guests, with Pedro tripping backwards and forwards with racks of toast and teapots, athletically stepping over a small ginger dog that had appeared in the hall to gaze longingly at us from the doorway.

My post-breakfast walk past all the elegant hotels left me in a quandary as to which would be best for my future stay. I could only make a decision after going through the list that Pedro had given me once I was home. So, the rest of the day was spent on a trip by tram to Fleetwood, then back to St Annes, spending loads of money in the process but realised that there was much to see in Lancashire.

Morning, and it was time for me to leave Blackpool until December. With a wave to Pedro and a promise to catch up at New Year, I was on my way home, excited to see how my place was looking after leaving Dave in charge. I was anxious, but not terribly so as I had confidence in the man. Of all the builders in all the world, I thought that I'd picked the best, so I don't know why I had this sense of foreboding. Probably because I was not at all sure how I was going to pay him.

November 4th

What a relief to get back home! It seemed as if I had been away for weeks. Dave had done a wonderful job restoring my place. All the fixtures and fittings put up by the film company had been removed as soon as the technical college had vacated the rooms and he had redecorated where necessary. My guest house looked pristine and workable again.

On the down side, S__ is quite dead now. Most of the SHAG group members are either doing up their places, have gone on holiday or are selling up after a dreadful season - some doing all three. I was not in a hurry to open again too soon myself, deciding out of season to open for Friday and Saturday nights only. I might make enough to pay the overheads, if I'm careful.

The second evening back, I decide to give Julian and Tristan a visit, see how they were getting on. Surprise, surprise! Without anyone's knowledge, they had put their place on the market and lined up a buyer at the full asking price. Consequently, they were already making plans and packing. They have decided to leave England for good and use their capital, after paying off their mortgage and loans, to buy or build a village property in Nandipur, Pakistan, in the district of Kokrajhar, some 156 miles from the state capital of Gauhati.

They had trekked this area many years ago and fell in love with the forest and friendly peoples. They thought they could open up a sort of cultural exploration and holiday centre there. Property was next to nothing to buy, and with the right connections in the UK for adventure holidays, they might clean up by being the first to try this.

Catching up with Raymond the following day, I found him busy building an outside plunge pool for his more fit guests next season. He seemed to be in high spirits, eager to pass on news about Norman and Fred from Dickeys Drive-In Hotel. There had been a serious fire at the building last Tuesday morning whilst the two of them were out swapping the laundry baskets at the hospital. Norman had left a chip pan on, expecting to be back within fifteen minutes, but the police were waiting for them behind the loading bay at the hospital and they were well and truly nabbed. What with that and the dodgy car with false number plates, it was off to the cells with them. In the meantime, their place burnt down. Completely. Further to the investigation of the cause of the fire, the rewired electricity and gas meters that had been tampered with were discovered, leading to more charges by the police. Out on bail, by the end of the week they had both disappeared. Some say they have done a runner across the channel.

A while later, sitting and wondering how I was going to pay Dave for all the work he had done, I was interrupted by the post arriving. Thumbing through the circulars and all the rubbish, there was a letter from my solicitor.

I am going to make myself a cup of tea with plenty of sugar before I read it…

Solicitor's Note

This is as far as Darryl has got. He replied to my letter enclosing the diary, saying that it might be of interest to the wider world, offering me full publishing rights, hoping that any funds recouped by the sale of said diary might go towards paying Dave the builder and numerous other creditors, including, not least, myself.

He also said, in some detail, that the hospitality business was too demanding a life, not for everyone. I would have liked to discuss this with him, as well as my fees and his debts, but he has vanished.

If he returns, I will let you know.